INTEGRAL CALCULUS

LIBRARY OF MATHEMATICS

edited by

WALTER LEDERMANN
D.Sc., Ph.D., F.R.S.Ed.
Reader in Mathematics, University of Sussex

Linear Equations	P. M. Cohn
Sequences and Series	J. A. Green
Differential Calculus	P. J. Hilton
Elementary Differential Equations and Operators	G. E. H. Reuter
Partial Derivatives	P. J. Hilton
Complex Numbers	W. Ledermann
Principles of Dynamics	M. B. Glauert
Electrical and Mechanical Oscillations	D. S. Jones
Vibrating Systems	R. F. Chisnell
Vibrating Strings	D. R. Bland
Fourier Series	I. N. Sneddon
Solutions of Laplace's Equation	D. R. Bland
Solid Geometry	P. M. Cohn
Numerical Approximation	B. R. Morton
Integral Calculus	W. Ledermann

INTEGRAL CALCULUS

BY
WALTER LEDERMANN

ROUTLEDGE AND KEGAN PAUL
LONDON

First published 1964
by Routledge & Kegan Paul Ltd
Broadway House, 68-74 Carter Lane
London, E.C.4

Printed in Great Britain
by W. & G. Baird Ltd
Belfast

Preface

It is assumed that the reader of this book is fairly proficient in the evaluation of elementary integrals by standard methods. A few examples for revision are included at the end of the first chapter, but no systematic exposition of techniques is given in the text.

At the other end of the scale of sophistication, I have omitted a rigorous treatment of the Riemann integral, but merely stated the basic existence theorem after a few explanatory remarks. Readable accounts of this theory are now easily accessible (see references on p. 3).

The purpose of the book is to give a reasonably self-contained account of the more advanced topics of the integral calculus, such as differentiation and integration under the integral sign. A large part of the work is devoted to the factorial function.

In order to reduce the weight of some of the arguments, I have made a number of concessions, not indeed to the standard of rigour expected at this level, but to the economy of hypotheses under which certain facts can be established. I trust, however, that the results proved are sufficiently realistic for practical purposes.

Despite this policy of compromise, a number of tricky points remained. Most of these are treated in Appendices which can be ignored by a reader who is more interested in the applications than in the proofs.

PREFACE

I am greatly indebted to Professor G. E. H. Reuter who has read the manuscript of the book and has made a number of valuable suggestions.

W. LEDERMANN

The University of Sussex,
Brighton.

Contents

Preface   *page* v

1. Single Integrals
   1. *Definition and existence*   1
   2. *The Fundamental Theorem*   8
   3. *Evaluation of single integrals*   10
   4. *Complex-valued functions*   14
   Exercises   16

2. Improper Integrals
   1. *Introductory remarks*   18
   2. *Unbounded integrands*   19
   3. *Infinite range of integration*   21
   Exercises   24

3. Functions defined by Integrals
   1. *Introduction*   27
   2. *Continuity*   27
   3. *Differentiation under the integral sign*   28
   4. *Integration under the integral sign*   33
   Exercises   39

4. The Factorial (Gamma) Function
   1. *Euler's Second Integral*   41
   2. *The Beta Function*   45
   3. *The product expansion of x!*   52
   4. *Stirling's formula*   56
   Exercises   60

CONTENTS

Appendix I	*page* 62
Appendix II	64
Appendix III	68
Appendix IV	70
Solutions for Exercises	74
List of formulae	80
Index	85

CHAPTER ONE
Single Integrals

---

1. DEFINITION AND EXISTENCE

It is assumed that the reader has a working knowledge of integrals involving functions of a single variable, and that he has acquired a fair degree of skill in evaluating such integrals. In § 3 we shall briefly recall the chief technical devices used in this task, which is often tricky and laborious, and at the end of this book (pp. 80-84) we have collected a list of formulae for reference.

As is well known, there are two ways of introducing the integral calculus. One method consists in presenting integration as the inverse of differentiation; that is, given a function $f(x)$, we seek a function $F(x)$ such that

$$F'(x) = f(x). \tag{1}$$

If such a function F exists, and there is *a priori* no reason why it should, it is customary to call it an *integral* of f, or better a *primitive* of f. It is clear that if F satisfies (1), then so does $F + c$, where c is an arbitrary constant, usually called the constant of integration.

The other approach is to define integration as an operation akin to summation. At first sight this method appears to be more difficult as it is based on a somewhat sophisticated limiting process. But the ideas involved are more fundamental and lend themselves more readily to generalisations than the inversion of differentiation.

1

We shall use this second approach as our starting point. But it will not be our aim in this book to give a rigorous theoretical treatment of integration. However, it is instructive to review, in an intuitive manner, the familiar introduction of single integrals. Consider the problem of determining the total mass of a straight wire of non-uniform density. In order to describe the situation in mathematical terms suppose the wire is placed along the x-axis and occupies the finite segment $[a,b]$, that is, it consists of all points x satisfying $a \leqq x \leqq b$. The *density at* x is a function of $f(x)$. Roughly speaking, this means that the mass of a small segment $[x_1,x_2]$ is 'approximately' equal to

$$f(x)(x_2 - x_1), \tag{2}$$

where $x_1 \leqq x \leqq x_2$ (see Fig. 1).

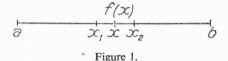

Figure 1.

We have used inverted commas to indicate concepts and arguments that serve only as a guidance and fall short of mathematical precision. The reader will observe that the exact position of the point x in the segment has been left open. In fact, the 'smallness' of the segment $[x_1,x_2]$ implies that the variation of $f(x)$ can be 'ignored' for our purpose. Thus if ξ is an arbitrary point of this segment, we should accept

$$f(\xi)(x_1 - x_2) \tag{3}$$

as an equally good approximation to its mass. In this way we obtain an approximate value of the total mass of the wire. All we have to do is to break up the wire into sufficiently 'small' segments. This means we make a subdivision Δ of $[a,b]$ by choosing points $x_1, x_2, \ldots, x_{n-1}$ such that

$$a = x_0 < x_1 < x_2 \ldots x_{n-1} < x_n = b$$

with the proviso that the subintervals $[x_{i-1}, x_i](i = 1, 2, \ldots, n)$ are so small that their masses are given by (3) with 'sufficient' accuracy. Thus in each subinterval we choose an arbitrary point ξ_i satisfying $x_{i-1} \leqq \xi_i \leqq x_i (i = 1, 2, \ldots, n)$. The total mass of the wire is then approximately equal to $\sum_{i=1}^{n} f(\xi_i)(x_i - x_{i-1})$. In order to pass from this approximation to a precise evaluation of the mass we introduce the *norm* δ of the subdivision Δ. It is defined by

$$\delta = \max_{1 \leqq i \leqq n} |x_i - x_{i-1}|,$$

that is, δ is the length of the largest subinterval occurring in the subdivision. In this way a positive number is associated with every subdivision. We now envisage an infinite set of subdivisions being performed whose norms tend to zero. The exact mass is then defined by

$$\lim_{\delta \to 0} \sum_{i=1}^{n} f(\xi_i)(x_i - x_{i-1}). \tag{4}$$

To be sure, this limit need not exist if f is a highly irregular function. But it is known to exist for a wide class of functions, which include the continuous functions. When the limit exists, it is called the (definite) integral of f over $[a, b]$ and is denoted by

$$\int_a^b f(x)dx.$$

This formal discussion describes the gist of the basic theorem*. For our purpose it suffices to formulate the result in a special case.

* J. C. Burkill, *A First Course in Mathematical Analysis* (Cambridge University Press), 119*ff*. E. G. Phillips, *A Course of Analysis* (Cambridge University Press), Chapter VII.

SINGLE INTEGRALS

Existence Theorem. *Let f be a function which is continuous at every point of the finite interval* [a,b], *except possibly at a finite number of points. Let*

$$\Delta : a = x_0 < x_1 < x_2 < \ldots x_{n-1} < x_n = b$$

be a subdivision of norm δ. In each subinterval $[x_{i-1}, x_i]$ *choose a number* ξ_i *and form the approximation sum*

$$S(\Delta) = \sum_{i=1}^{n} f(\xi_i)(x_i - x_{i-1}).$$

Then, as Δ *runs through a set of subdivisions for which* δ *tends to zero,* S(Δ) *tends to a limit, called the integral of* f(x) *from a to b, in symbols,*

$$\lim_{\delta \to 0} S(\Delta) = \int_a^b f(x)dx.$$

Moreover, this limit does not depend on the choice of ξ_i *in* $[x_{i-1}, x_i]$ *or on the set of subdivisions.*

This is the fundamental theorem from which all the properties of the integral can be deduced. We shall show in a subsequent volume that the idea of an integral as the limit of approximating sums can be extended to more general situations. The very notation underlines the affinity of integration with summation. For the ∫ sign is simply an elongated S, the symbol formerly used for summation; also the difference of two 'adjacent' values of x used to be written dx.

We have referred to the concept of density to motivate the notion of a definite integral. There are other intuitive ideas that can serve the same purpose. The best known example is the area bounded by a section of the curve $y = f(x)$, the axis of x and the lines $x = a$, $x = b$, where $a \leqq b$. As the reader will be aware, this area is given by $\int_a^b f(x)\,dx$. One might be tempted to define the integral as this area.

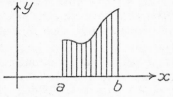

Figure 2.

However, this approach to integration is based on the assumption that we know what is meant by the area of a region that is partly or wholly bounded by curves. A rigorous definition of area is beyond the scope of this book, and is in fact equivalent to a rigorous definition of an integral. We prefer to accept the analytical definition of an integral inherent in the Existence Theorem of p. 4 and to define area, in its turn, by means of an appropriate integral.

In the construction of an integral between the limits a and b, it was naturally assumed that $a < b$. In order to remove this restriction we put

$$\int_a^b f(x)\,dx = -\int_b^a f(x)\,dx \qquad (5)$$

We omit the proofs of the following general rules which can easily be deduced from the definition:

(i) $\displaystyle\int_a^c f(x)\,dx + \int_c^b f(x)\,dx = \int_a^b f(x)\,dx.$

(ii) $\displaystyle\int_a^b \{f(x) + g(x)\}\,dx = \int_a^b f(x)\,dx + \int_a^b g(x)\,dx$

(iii) $\displaystyle\int_a^b k\,f(x)\,dx = k\int_a^b f(x)\,dx,$ where k is a constant.

We would remind the reader that the value of the integral does not depend on the notation employed for the variable of integration, which, in other words, is a *dummy* variable thus $\int_a^b f(x)\,dx = \int_a^b f(t)\,dt$. But we urge him to avoid the clumsy clash of notation perpetrated in such formulae as $\int_a^x f(x)\,dx$, in place of $\int_a^x f(t)\,dt$, say.

Several important inequalities about integrals follow almost immediately from the definition. It is obvious that, when $f(x) \geqq 0$ in $[a,b]$, then $S(\Delta) \geqq 0$ for every Δ, and hence, in the limit,

$$\int_a^b f(x)\,dx \geqq 0. \tag{6}$$

More generally, if $h(x) \leqq f(x) \leqq g(x)$ in $[a,b]$, the functions $f - h$ and $g - f$ are non-negative in $[a,b]$. On applying (6) we deduce that

$$\int_a^b h(x)\,dx \leqq \int_a^b f(x)\,dx \leqq \int_a^b g(x)\,dx.$$

In other words, inequalities between functions may be integrated. In particular, since

$$- \left| f(x) \right| \leqq f(x) \leqq \left| f(x) \right|,$$

it follows that $- \int_a^b |f(x)|\,dx \leqq \int_a^b f(x)\,dx \leqq \int_a^b |f(x)|\,dx$, that is

$$\left| \int_a^b f(x)\,dx \right| \leqq \int_a^b |f(x)|\,dx. \tag{7}$$

Our assumption with regard to continuity implies that f is bounded in $[a,b]$, that is, there exist constants m and M such that

$$m \leqq f(x) \leqq M \qquad (a \leqq x \leqq b). \tag{8}$$

On integrating this inequality over $[a,b]$ we find that

$$m(b - a) \leqq \int_a^b f(x)dx \leqq M(b - a). \qquad (9)$$

A somewhat more general result is obtained as follows: let $\phi(x)$ be a non-negative function in $[a,b]$. Multiply (8) throughout by $\phi(x)$ and integrate, thus

$$m \int_a^b \phi(x)dx \leqq \int_a^b f(x)\phi(x)dx \leqq M \int_a^b \phi(x)dx. \qquad (10)$$

Further deductions can be made from (9) and (10), if f is (strictly) continuous in $[a,b]$, that is free from jump-discontinuities. For a continuous function attains every value between the least and greatest value taken by it. Thus if m and M are the minimum and the maximum of $f(x)$ in the interval $[a,b]$, the inequalities (9) state that $(b - a)^{-1} \int_a^b f(x)\,dx$ lies between m and M. Hence there exists at least one value, ξ, in $[a,b]$ such that

$$\int_a^b f(x)dx = f(\xi)(b - a). \qquad (11)$$

Applying a similar argument to (10), we conclude that there is at least one value in $[a,b]$, say η, such that

$$\int_a^b f(x)\phi(x)dx = f(\eta) \int_a^b \phi(x)dx, \qquad (12)$$

provided that ϕ is non-negative in $[a,b]$. Formula (11) or (12) is usually referred to as the *First Mean Value Theorem* of the integral calculus*.

*The Second Mean Value Theorem will not be introduced in this book.

7

2. THE FUNDAMENTAL THEOREM

The definition of an integral as a limit of approximation sums does not readily lead to the evaluation of particular integrals, except in special circumstances. The fact that integration and differentiation are inverse operations provides a much more powerful tool for achieving this aim. Since we have introduced integration without reference to differentiation, the reciprocity of the two calculi constitutes a theorem that has to be proved. It is indeed the cornerstone of the whole edifice and rightly deserves the name of *Fundamental Theorem* of the Integral Calculus. Let f be a function in $[a,b]$ and suppose the function F has the property that

$$F'(x) = f(x) \text{ in } [a,b]. \tag{13}$$

Then the theorem asserts that

$$\int_a^b f(x)dx = F(b) - F(a). \tag{14}$$

It is convenient to use the abbreviation $[F(x)]_a^b = F(b) - F(a)$. As we have already remarked, a function having the property (13) is called a primitive of f. Clearly, it follows from (14) that, if we can find a primitive of f, the integration of f is instantly accomplished.

Let us first consider some consequences of the Fundamental Theorem. In (14) the upper limit of integration may be replaced by an arbitrary number, x, in $[a,b]$. Changing the variable of integration to t, we can write

$$F(x) = F(a) + \int_a^x f(t)dt \qquad (a \leqq x \leqq b).$$

On differentiating both sides with respect to x we obtain the important result that

$$\frac{d}{dx} \int_a^x f(t)dt = f(x). \tag{15}$$

Thus the derivative of an integral with respect to its upper limit is the value of the integral at the upper limit. It is customary to denote the integral $\int_a^x f(t)\,dt$ by

$$\int f(x)dx$$

whatever the value of the lower limit and to call it the *indefinite integral* of f. The indefinite integral is determined only up to an additive constant, the constant of integration, and it may be equated to a primitive.

The Fundamental Theorem may be proved directly from the Existence Theorem as follows: let Δ be a subdivision of $[a,b]$, as described on p. 3 and suppose that F has the property (13). By the Mean Value Theorem of the Differential Calculus* there exists at least one number ξ_i in the subinterval $[x_{i-1},x_i]$ such that

$$F(x_i) - F(x_{i-1}) = F'(\xi_i)(x_i - x_{i-1})$$
$$= f(\xi_i)(x_i - x_{i-1}) \ (i = 1,2, ..., n).$$

We now choose, as we may, these values ξ_i in order to form the approximation sum $S(\Delta)$ which is associated with Δ. Then

$$S(\Delta) = \sum_{i=1}^n f(\xi_i)(x_i - x_{i-1})$$
$$= \sum_{i=1}^n \{F(x_i) - F(x_{i-1})\} = F(b) - F(a).$$

* P. J. Hilton, *Differential Calculus*, in this series, p. 34.

Since the expression on the right does not depend on Δ, it follows that

$$\lim_{\delta \to 0} S(\Delta) = \int_a^b f(x)dx = F(b) - F(a).$$

This proves the theorem.

The following example illustrates a procedure that might be called integration from first principles.

Example. Prove that

$$\lim_{n \to \infty} \sum_{k=1}^n \frac{n}{n^2 + k^2} = \frac{\pi}{4}.$$

We shall evaluate the integral $\int_0^1 \dfrac{dx}{1 + x^2} = \tan^{-1}(1) = \dfrac{\pi}{4}$

directly from the definition. Let Δ be the subdivision of $[0,1]$ in which $x_k = k/n$, where n is an arbitrary positive integer and $k = 1,2,\ldots,n$. For ξ_k choose the value k/n. The corresponding approximation sum then becomes

$$S(\Delta) = \sum_{k=1}^n \frac{1}{1 + (k/n)^2} \frac{1}{n} = \sum_{k=1}^n \frac{n}{n^2 + k^2}.$$

Since the norm of Δ is clearly $1/n$, the integral is equal to the limit of this sum when n tends to infinity.

3. EVALUATION OF SINGLE INTEGRALS

It is not our object to deal at length with the technique of integration, of which the reader, no doubt, has had some more or less pleasant prior experience. Broadly speaking, every

1.3 EVALUATION OF SINGLE INTEGRALS

formula of differentiation can be turned into a result on integration. Thus

$$\int x^2 dx = x^3/3, \text{ because } \frac{d}{dx}x^3/3 = x^2$$

$$\int \frac{dx}{\sqrt{(a^2 - x^2)}} = \sin^{-1}(x/a) \ (a > 0),$$

because $\frac{d}{dx}\sin^{-1}(x/a) = \frac{1}{\sqrt{(a^2 - x^2)}}$.

When writing indefinite integrals we shall, as a rule, suppress the constant of integration. It is therefore possible to obtain two different results for the same integral, the difference being due to an additive constant.

Thus the last result may equally well be written

$$\int \frac{dx}{\sqrt{(a^2 - x^2)}} = -\cos^{-1}(x/a) \ (a > 0).$$

Special care is needed when many-valued functions, such as $\sin^{-1} x$, are used.

In practice, elementary integration is based on a knowledge of standard integrals, some of which are listed on p. 80. Three general principles are available to reduce a given integral to standard types.

(1) The properties of integration, expressed in the rules (ii) and (iii) of p. 5 allow us to integrate a finite sum of functions term by term and to extract constant factors.

(2) *Integration by parts, namely,*

$$u\frac{dv}{dx}dx = uv - v\frac{du}{dx}dx$$

11

replaces the problem of integrating $u \dfrac{du}{dv}$ by that of integrating $v \dfrac{du}{dx}$, which may be simpler.

(3) *Change of the variable of integration*. This is the integral version of the formula* $\dfrac{dy}{dx} = \dfrac{dy}{dz}\dfrac{dz}{dx}$ for differentiating a function of a function. In view of later generalizations it is worth while recalling this important procedure in more detail. If we attempt to evaluate the indefinite integral $\int f(x)dx$ by the substitution

$$x = \phi(u) \qquad (16)$$

we obtain that

$$\int f(x)dx = \int f(\phi(u))\phi'(u)du$$

and hope that the integral on the right is easier to handle than the integral on the left. It must be stressed that only those substitutions (16) are admissible for which ϕ' is continuous and *non-zero*, except at a finite number of places. This ensures that (16) can be solved unambiguously for u, so that ϕ possesses a single-valued inverse function $u = \phi^{-1}(x)$. For the transformation of a definite integral we have the formula

$$\int_a^b f(x)dx = \int_\alpha^\beta f(\phi(u))\phi'(u)du,$$

where α and β are defined by $\alpha = \phi^{-1}(a)$ and $\beta = \phi^{-1}(b)$ respectively. Thus a change of variable in a definite integral involves three steps:

(1) introduce a new variable of integration by means of an invertible substitution $x = \phi(u)$, $u = \phi^{-1}(x)$

(2) transform the differential by putting $dx = \phi'(u)du$

* Hilton, *loc. cit.*, pp. 18-19.

12

(3) change the limits of integration from a, b to $\phi^{-1}(a)$, $\phi^{-1}(b)$.

In some cases, when the integral involves one or more arbitrary integers as parameters, the integral can be evaluated with the help of a *reduction formula*. As a typical example we consider the integral

$$I(m,n) = \int \sin^m x \cos^n x \, dx, \tag{17}$$

where m and n are non-negative integers. It is convenient to use the abbreviations $s = \sin x, c = \cos x$. Assume first that $m \geqq 2$. Write $s^m c^n = s^{m-1}(-c^{n+1}/n+1)'$. Integrating by parts we find that

$$I(m,n) = \frac{-s^{m-1}c^{n+1}}{n+1} + \frac{m-1}{n+1}I(m-2,n+2).$$

But $c^{n+2} = c^n - s^2 c^n$. Hence $I(m-2,n+2) = I(m-2,n) - I(m,n)$. On eliminating $I(m-2,n+2)$ and collecting terms we obtain the reduction formula

$$I(m,n) = \frac{-s^{m-1}c^{n+1}}{n+m} + \frac{m-1}{n+m}I(m-2,n)$$

$$(m \geqq 2, n \geqq 0) \tag{18}$$

Similarly, by reducing the exponent of $\cos x$,

$$I(m,n) = \frac{s^{m+1}c^{n-1}}{n+m} + \frac{n-1}{n+m}I(m,n-2) \quad (m \geqq 0, n \geqq 2) \tag{19}$$

From (18) and (19) we can deduce reduction formulae for definite integrals. For example, consider the integrals

$$S_n = \int_0^{\pi/2} \sin^n x \, dx, \quad C_n = \int_0^{\pi/2} \cos^n x \, dx.$$

If $n \geqq 2$, we can use (18) and (19) and find that

$$S_n = \left[\frac{-s^{n-1}c}{n} \right]_0^{\pi/2} + \frac{n-1}{n} S_{n-2} = \frac{n-1}{n} S_{n-2},$$

$$C_n = \left[\frac{sc^{n-1}}{n} \right]_0^{\pi/2} + \frac{n-1}{n} C_{n-2} = \frac{n-1}{n} C_{n-2}.$$

By direct computation we verify that $S_0 = C_0 = \pi/2$, $S_1 = C_1 = 1$. Since S_n and C_n satisfy the same recurrence relation for $n \geqq 2$, it follows that they are equal for all $n (\geqq 0)$. By repeated use of the recurrence relation we obtain the result that

$$\int_0^{\pi/2} \sin^n x \, dx = \int_0^{\pi/2} \cos^n x \, dx$$

$$= \begin{cases} \dfrac{(n-1)(n-3) \dots 3}{n(n-2) \dots 2} \dfrac{\pi}{2} & \text{if } n \text{ is even} \\[2ex] \dfrac{(n-1)(n-3) \dots 2}{n(n-2) \dots 3} & \text{if } n \text{ is odd and } \geqq 3. \end{cases} \qquad (20)$$

4. COMPLEX-VALUED FUNCTIONS

Situations arise in which a function of a real variable takes complex values*. Such a function can be expressed in the form

$$F(t) = f(t) + ig(t),$$

where f and g are real-valued functions of t. The derivative of F is defined by

$$F'(t) = f'(t) + ig'(t),$$

and it is easily verified that the following rules hold:

(i) $\dfrac{d}{dt}(F + G) = F' + G'$

(ii) $\dfrac{d}{dt}(\alpha F) = \alpha F',$

* See the author's *Complex Numbers*, in this series.

14

where G is another complex-valued function and α is a complex constant. For example, in order to prove the second rule, put $\alpha = a + ib$. Then

$$\frac{d}{dt}(\alpha F) = \frac{d}{dt}\{(af - bg) + i(ag + bf)\}$$

$$= (af' - bg') + i(ag' + bf')$$

$$= (a + ib)(f' + ig') = \alpha F'.$$

Similarly, integration is defined in the obvious way, namely by putting

$$\int F(t)dt = \int f(t)dt + i \int g(t)dt,$$

and it is clear that

(i) $\int (F + G)dt = \int F dt + \int G dt,$

(ii) $\int \alpha F dt = \alpha \int F dt.$

For example the formulae

$$\frac{d}{dt}e^{\alpha t} = \alpha e^{\alpha t}, \quad \int e^{\alpha t}dt = \frac{1}{\alpha}e^{\alpha t} \ (\alpha \neq 0)$$

are still valid, when α is a complex number. Writing $\alpha = a + ib$ and resolving the second formula into real and imaginary parts we obtain the results

$$\int e^{at}\cos bt \, dt = e^{at}\frac{a \cos bt + b \sin bt}{a^2 + b^2} \tag{21}$$

$$\int e^{at}\sin bt \, dt = e^{at}\frac{a \sin bt - b \cos bt}{a^2 + b^2}, \tag{22}$$

the constant of integration being omitted in each case.

15

SINGLE INTEGRALS
EXERCISES ON CHAPTER ONE

1. Use integration from first principles to establish the following results.

   (i) $\lim\limits_{n \to \infty} (1^s + 2^s + \dots + n^s)/n^{s+1} = 1/s + 1 \qquad (s \neq -1)$

   (ii) $\lim\limits_{n \to \infty} \left\{ \dfrac{1}{n + 1} + \dfrac{1}{n + 2} + \dots + \dfrac{1}{2n} \right\} = \log 2$

   (iii) $\lim\limits_{n \to \infty} \dfrac{1}{n^{\frac{1}{2}}} \{ (a + n)^{-\frac{1}{2}} + (2a + n)^{-\frac{1}{2}} + (3a + n)^{-\frac{1}{2}}$

   $+ \dots + (na + n)^{-\frac{1}{2}} \} = \dfrac{2}{a} \{ (a + 1)^{\frac{1}{2}} - 1 \} \qquad (a \neq 0).$

2. Prove the following reduction formulae

   (i) If $I_n = \displaystyle\int_0^\pi x^n \cos x \, dx$, $I_n = -n\pi^{n-1} - n(n - 1)I_{n-2} \quad (n \geqq 2)$

   (ii) If $T_n = \displaystyle\int \tan^n x \, dx$, $T_n = \dfrac{\tan^{n-1} x}{n - 1} - T_{n-2} \qquad (n \neq 1)$

   (iii) If $J_n = \displaystyle\int_0^{2a} x^n (2ax - x^2)^{\frac{1}{2}} dx$, $J_n = \dfrac{2n + 1}{n + 2} a J_{n-1}$

   (iv) If $P_{m,n} = \displaystyle\int \cos^m x \sin nx \, dx \quad (n \neq 0)$, show that
   $$(m + n)P_{n,m} = -\cos^m x \cos nx + m P_{m-1,n-1}.$$

   Prove that $\displaystyle\int_0^{\pi/2} \cos^m x \sin mx \, dx = 2^{-m-1} \left(\dfrac{2}{1} + \dfrac{2^2}{2} + \dfrac{2^3}{3} + \dots + \dfrac{2^m}{m} \right).$

   (v) If $L_n = \displaystyle\int x^\alpha (\log x)^n dx \quad (\alpha \neq -1)$, show that
   $$L_n = \dfrac{x^{\alpha+1}}{\alpha + 1} (\log x)^n - \dfrac{n}{\alpha + 1} L_{n-1}.$$

   Prove that, if $\alpha > 0$, $\displaystyle\int_0^1 x^\alpha (\log x)^n dx = (-1)^n n! (\alpha + 1)^{-n-1}.$

EXERCISES

3. Evaluate the following integrals

(i) $\int (e^{2x} + e^x)^{\frac{1}{2}} dx$, (ii) $\int (1 - 3x - x^2)^{\frac{1}{2}} dx$, (iii) $\int \dfrac{dx}{x(x^2 + x - 6)^{\frac{1}{2}}}$,

(iv) $\int \dfrac{1 - 3x^2}{3x - x^3} dx$, (v) $\int \dfrac{(x + 1)dx}{x^2 + 10x - 75}$, (vi) $\int \exp(a \sin^{-1} x) dx$.

4. Show that $\displaystyle\int_0^{\pi/4} (\tan\theta)^{\frac{1}{2}} d\theta = \dfrac{1}{2\sqrt{2}} \{\pi + 2\log(\sqrt{2} - 1)\}$.

5. Point out the fallacy in the following argument: let $A = \displaystyle\int_{-1}^1 \dfrac{dx}{1 + x^2}$

(in fact $A = [\tan^{-1} x]_{-1}^1 = \frac{1}{2}\pi$), put $x = y^{-1}$, whence $A =$

$-\displaystyle\int_{-1}^1 \dfrac{dy}{y^2} \dfrac{1}{1 + y^{-2}}$, $A = -\displaystyle\int_{-1}^1 \dfrac{dy}{1 + y^2} = -A$, $A = 0$.

17

CHAPTER TWO
Improper Integrals

1. INTRODUCTORY REMARKS

In the definition of the integral

$$\int_a^b f(x)dx$$

described in the preceding chapter, it was assumed that

(i) the integrand, f, was bounded and sufficiently well behaved, for example continuous except, at most, at a finite number of points, and

(ii) the range of integration was finite.

If one or the other of these conditions is violated, the integral may fail to exist. But in certain circumstances it is nevertheless possible to extend the definition of an integral so as to cover cases of this kind. Such integrals are termed *improper integrals*. Basically, we shall be concerned with only two kinds of improper integral, according as condition (i) or (ii) above ceases to hold. However both complications may occur together.

We shall not develop a systematic theory of improper integrals, but shall be content with a discussion of a few typical cases.

The following example may serve as a warning that the restrictions on the integrand cannot be disregarded with impunity. Formal, but thoughtless, manipulation might lead to the result that $\int_{-1}^{1} \frac{dx}{x^2} = \left[-\frac{1}{x} \right]_{-1}^{1} = -2$, which is clearly absurd since the integrand is never negative. As a matter of fact, the integrand is not defined at $x = 0$ and is unbounded in the range of integration.

2. UNBOUNDED INTEGRANDS

For simplicity, we take the range of integration to be the interval $[0,a]$, where a is finite, and we suppose that the point $x = 0$ is the sole singularity of f. More precisely, we assume that $f(x)$ is continuous in $[\delta,a]$, where δ is any number such that $0 < \delta < a$, but that

$$\lim_{x \to 0} f(x) = \infty.$$

Then $I(\delta) = \int_\delta^a f(x)\,dx$ certainly exists. If now $I(\delta)$ tends to a finite limit, as δ tends to zero, we define

$$\int_0^a f(x)\,dx = \lim_{\delta \to 0} I(\delta). \qquad (1)$$

If the limit on the right-hand side of (1) does not exist, the improper integral $\int_0^a f(x)\,dx$ does not exist or is said to *diverge*.

The situation is in many ways analogous to the summation of infinite series. The following simple rules* are almost immediate consequences of the definition.

(1) Let $f(x)$ and $g(x)$ be functions whose only singularity in $[a,b]$ is at $x = 0$. If $\int_0^a f(x)\,dx$ and $\int_0^a g(x)\,dx$ converge so do the integrals $\int_0^a \{f(x) + g(x)\}\,dx$, $\int_0^a \{f(x) - g(x)\}\,dx$ and $\int_0^a kf(x)\,dx$, where k is a constant, and

$$\int_0^a \{f(x) \pm g(x)\}\,dx = \int_0^a f(x)\,dx \pm \int_0^a g(x)\,dx,$$

$$\int_0^a kf(x)\,dx = k\int_0^a f(x)\,dx.$$

* J. A. Green, *Sequences and Series*, in this series, pp. 30 and 34.

When the integrand is non-negative in the range of integration the problem is simpler. For in that case $I(\delta)$ increases monotonically, as δ tends to zero through positive values. Hence $I(\delta)$ either increases beyond all bounds or else tends to a finite limit. Thus, if we can prove that there exists a number M such that $I(\delta) < M$ for all δ $(0 < \delta < a)$, then the convergence of the improper integral is guaranteed. Also, we have the analogue of the comparison test for non-negative series:

(2) Let $u(x)$ and $v(x)$ be non-negative functions such that $u(x) \leqq v(x)$ for all x satisfying $0 < x < a$, and assume that $\int_0^a v(x)\,dx$ exists. Then $\int_0^a u(x)\,dx$ exists.

We omit the formal proof.

(3) It is now an easy matter to establish the rule that, if $\int_0^a |f(x)|\,dx$ exists, so does $\int_0^a f(x)\,dx$, that is absolute convergence (of an integral) implies ordinary convergence. For

$$u(x) = \tfrac{1}{2}\{|f(x)| + f(x)\} \text{ and } v(x) = \tfrac{1}{2}\{|f(x)| - f(x)\}$$

are non-negative functions satisfying $u(x) \leqq |f(x)|$ and $v(x) \leqq |f(x)|$ for all x. Since $|f|$ is integrable over $[0,a]$, so are u and v, and hence also their difference, that is $u - v = f$. This completes the proof.

Example 1. The integral $\displaystyle\int_0^a \frac{dx}{x^\lambda}$ $(a > 0)$ exists and has the value $a^{1-\lambda}/1 - \lambda$, if $\lambda < 1$, but does not exist if $\lambda \geqq 1$.

For if $\lambda \neq 1$, $I(\delta) = (a^{1-\lambda} - \delta^{1-\lambda})/1 - \lambda$, and it is clear that $\lim_{\delta \to 0} I(\delta)$ exists and is equal to $a^{1-\lambda}$, if $\lambda < 1$ and does not exist if $\lambda < 1$. Finally, if $\lambda = 1$, $I(\delta) = \log(a/\delta)$, whence it follows that $\lim I(\delta)$ does not exist in this case.

Example 2. If $g(x)$ is non-negative and continuous in $[0,a]$, then $\int_0^a \dfrac{g(x)}{x^\lambda}\,dx$ exists, if $\lambda < 1$. For our hypothesis implies that g is bounded in $[0,a]$, that is, there exists a number M such that $0 \leqq g(x) \leqq M$ for all x in $[0,a]$. Hence

$$\int_0^a \frac{g(x)}{x^\lambda}\,dx \leqq M \int_0^a \frac{dx}{x^\lambda} \qquad .$$

The existence of the integral on the left now follows at once as a consequence of the comparison test.

Example 3. In the integral

$$B(x,y) = \int_0^1 t^{x-1}(1-t)^{y-1}\,dt \quad (x > 0,\, y > 0)$$

the integrand is singular at $t = 0$, if $x < 1$ and is singular at $t = 1$, if $y < 1$. The integral certainly exists if the two integrals

$$\int_0^a t^{x-1}(1-t)^{y-1}\,dt,\; \int_a^1 t^{x-1}(1-t)^{y-1}\,dt$$

exist separately, where a is any number between 0 and 1. The first of these integrals converges by the preceding example, and the second integral is reduced to the same type by the substitution $t = 1 - s$.

3. INFINITE RANGE OF INTEGRATION

We consider the simple case in which $f(x)$ is continuous in every interval of the form $[a,X]$, where a is fixed and X is an arbitrary positive number. Then

$$I(X) = \int_a^X f(x)\,dx$$

certainly exists. If $I(X)$ tends to a finite limit as X tends to infinity, we define

$$\int_a^\infty f(x)dx = \lim_{x \to \infty} I(X).$$

If the limit does not exist, we say that the integral on the left does not exist, or that it *diverges*.

The general rules stated on p. 19 hold in this case with the obvious modification that the limits of integration have to be changed to a and ∞. In particular, we have a comparison test for non-negative integrands when the range is infinite.

Example 4. The integral $\int_a^\infty \dfrac{dx}{x^\lambda} (a > 0)$ exists and has the value

$a^{1-\lambda}/\lambda - 1$, if $\lambda > 1$, but does not exist if $\lambda \leqq 1$. Assume first

that $\lambda \neq 1$. Then $I(X) = \int_a^X \dfrac{dx}{x^\lambda} = (X^{1-\lambda} - a^{1-\lambda})/(1 - \lambda)$, and

it is clear that the right-hand side tends to a finite limit when $\lambda > 1$, but that it tends to infinity when $\lambda < 1$. Finally, when $\lambda = 1$, $I(X) = \log(X/a)$, which does not tend to a finite limit as $X \to \infty$. This establishes the result.

Example 5. Suppose that $g(x)$ is continuous, non-negative and bounded for $x \geqq a$. Thus there exists a number M such that

$0 \leqq g(x) \leqq M$ for all $x \geqq a$. Then the integral $\int_a^\infty \dfrac{g(x)}{x} dx$

converges, provided that $\lambda > 1$. The proof is similar to that given in Example 2 of § 2.

Example 6. The integral $\int_a^\infty \dfrac{\sin x}{x} dx$ converges. (Its value will be found later, see p. 38). The function $(\sin x)/x$ remains continuous at $x = 0$, if we define $(\sin x)/x = 1$ when $x = 0$.

Therefore no difficulty arises about the integral $\int_0^1 \frac{\sin x}{x}\, dx$,

and it suffices to prove the convergence of $\int_1^\infty \frac{\sin x}{x}\, dx$. Integrating by parts we find that

$$\int_1^X \frac{\sin x}{x}\, dx = \left[\frac{-\cos x}{x} \right]_1^X + \int_1^X \frac{\cos x}{x^2}\, dx.$$

As $X \to \infty$, the first term on the right tends to $+\cos 1$, and the integral on the right converges in virtue of the result established in Example 5.

It is interesting to observe that this is an instance of a *conditionally convergent* integral, that is $\int_1^\infty \frac{|\sin x|}{x}\, dx$ diverges.

For if this integral were finite, say equal to L, the infinite series

$$\sum_{r=0}^\infty \int_{\pi/4 + 2\pi_r}^{\pi/2 + 2\pi_r} \frac{|\sin x|}{x}\, dx$$

would converge, since its nth partial sum would be less than $\int_{\pi/4}^{\pi/2 + 2\pi n} \frac{|\sin x|}{x}\, dx$ and hence less than L. However, the rth term of this series is greater than $\sin(\pi/4)(\pi/2 + 2\pi r)^{-1}$, and the sum of these terms behaves like $\Sigma(1/r)$ and hence diverges.

Our final example deals with an important integral, whose properties will be studied in Chapter IV.

23

Example 7. The integral $\int_0^\infty t^x e^{-t}\,dt$, exists, provided that

$x > -1$. If $x < 0$, the integrand is singular at $t = 0$. It is therefore convenient to discuss separately the integrals

$$\int_0^1 t^x e^{-t}\,dt \text{ and } \int_1^\infty t^x e^{-t}\,dt.$$

The first of these integrals is of the form $\int_0^1 \frac{g(t)\,dt}{t^\lambda}$ and con-

verges by Example 2, p. 20; for $0 < g(t) = e^{-t} < 1$ and $\lambda = -x < 1$, because $x > -1$. As regards the second integral, we observe that, if $t > 0$,

$$e^t = 1 + \frac{t}{1!} + \frac{t^2}{2!} + \ldots + \frac{t^k}{k!} + \ldots > \frac{t^k}{k!},$$

where k is any positive integer we like to choose. Hence $t^x e^{-t} < k!/t^{k-x}$, and if we take k to be greater than $x + 1$, the convergence of the second integral can be deduced from Example 5 on p. 22.

EXERCISES ON CHAPTER TWO

1. Decide the convergence or divergence of the following integrals:

(i) $\int_0^1 x^{-\frac{1}{2}} \cos x\,dx$, (ii) $\int_0^2 (\sin x)^{-\frac{1}{2}}\,dx$, (iii) $\int_1^\infty (x^4 + x + 1)^{-\frac{1}{2}}\,dx$,

(iv) $\int_0^1 (x^2 - 1)^{-1}\,dx$, (v) $\int_0^\infty e^{x - x^2}\,dx$, (vi) $\int_0^{\pi/2} (\tan x)^{\frac{1}{2}}\,dx$.

EXERCISES

2. Prove that $\int_0^\infty \dfrac{x^{p-1}}{1+x}\,dx$ exists when $0 < p < 1$. [Hint: break the range of integration at $x = 1$, and express the integral as the sum of two integrals.]

   Prove that $\int_0^\infty \dfrac{x^{\alpha-1}}{1+x^\beta}\,dx$ converges, if $0 < \alpha < \beta$.

3. Show that the integral $\int_0^\pi \dfrac{dx}{(\sin x)^\lambda}$ converges if $0 < \lambda < 1$.

   [Note that the integrand tends to infinity at either end of the range of integration.]

4. Prove that $\int_0^\infty \dfrac{1 - (1+s)e^{-s}}{s^2}\,ds$ converges.

5. Prove that $\int_0^\infty \dfrac{\sqrt{x}\,dx}{1+x^2} = \dfrac{\pi}{\sqrt{2}}$.

6. Show that $\int_0^\infty \dfrac{x\,dx}{(1+x)(1+x^2)} = \dfrac{\pi}{4}$.

7. Prove that $\int_0^\infty f(x)\,dx = \int_0^1 \{f(x) + x^{-2}f(x^{-1})\}\,dx$.

8. Prove that $\int_2^\infty \dfrac{dx}{(\log x)^\alpha}$ diverges for all values of α.

9. Prove that $\int_2^\infty \dfrac{dx}{x(\log x)^\alpha}$ converges if $\alpha > 1$ and diverges for all other values of α.

10. For what values of k does the integral $\int_0^\infty \dfrac{dx}{(x + x^4)^k}$ converge?

C

25

11. Show that $\displaystyle\int_0^\pi \frac{d\theta}{1 + a\cos\theta} = \pi(1 - a^2)^{-\frac{1}{2}}$ $(|a| < 1)$.

CHAPTER THREE
Functions defined by Integrals

---

1. INTRODUCTION

On several occasions we have met definite integrals, in which the integrand depends on one or more parameters (see Examples 1 and 3 on p. 20/21). In some cases the parameter is restricted to a limited range, but within this range the integral defines a function of the parameter.

In this Chapter we shall be concerned with general properties of functions defined by integrals. In particular, we shall investigate their continuity, differentiability and integrability. Confining ourselves to a single parameter for the time being, we shall use the notation

$$F(x) = \int_{\alpha}^{\beta} f(x,t)dt \quad (a \leqq x \leqq b) \tag{1}$$

for a typical function defined by an integral. It is assumed that the integral (with respect to t) has a finite value for each permissible value of x, say for $a \leqq x \leqq b$. In some of the most interesting cases a further complication arises through the fact that the integral is an improper integral in the sense of Chapter II. In order to allow for this possibility we are not assuming that the range of integration, $[\alpha,\beta]$, in (1) is finite.

2. CONTINUITY

It can be shown that, under rather liberal conditions on f, the function F defined in (1) is a continuous function of x.

However, it is not our ambition to establish this and similar results on the weakest hypotheses that are known. The proofs of some of these theorems would then certainly be beyond the scope of this book. For a more detailed discussion of these questions the reader is referred to standard works on Analysis. *
Nevertheless, we shall present at least one theorem, however crude, on each of the main properties of $F(x)$.

Theorem 1. *The function F defined in* (1) *is continuous in the interval* $[a,b]$, *if there exists a function $\phi(t)$ such that*†

(i) $|f_x(x,t)| \leqq \phi(t)$ *for all x in* $[a,b]$ *and all t in* $[\alpha,\beta]$

(ii) $\int_\alpha^\beta \phi(t)dt$ *is finite.*

Proof: We have to show that $\lim_{h \to 0} \{F(x + h) - F(x)\} = 0$. Now, for fixed t, the function $f(x,t)$ is a function of x only. Applying the Mean Value Theorem of the Differential Calculus for this case we find that $f(x + h,t) - f(x,t) = hf_x(x + \theta h,t)$, where θ lies between 0 and 1 and in general depends on x, h and t. On using the two hypotheses of the theorem we obtain that

$$\left|F(x + h) - F(x)\right| = |h| \left| \int_\alpha^\beta f_x(x + \theta h,t)dt \right| \leqq |h| \int_\alpha^\beta \phi(t)dt,$$

whence $\lim_{h \to 0} \{F(x + h) - F(x)\} = 0$.

3. DIFFERENTIATION UNDER THE INTEGRAL SIGN

More stringent conditions on f are required to ensure that F is a differentiable function of x.

Theorem 2. *Let F be defined by* (1) *and assume that there exists a function $\psi(t)$ such that*

*e.g. R. Courant, *Differential and Integral Calculus* (Blackie & Son, Glasgow), vol. II, 217*ff*.

† We write f_x for the partial derivative.

3.3 DIFFERENTIATION UNDER INTEGRAL SIGN

(i) $|f_{xx}(x,t)| \leqq \psi(t)$ for all x in $[a,b]$ and all t in $[\alpha,\beta]$

(ii) $\displaystyle\int_{\alpha}^{\beta} \psi(t)dt$ is finite, equal to M, say.

Then F is a differentiable function of x in $[a,b]$ and

$$\frac{dF}{dx} = \int_{\alpha}^{\beta} f_x(x,t)dt,$$

that is the integral may be differentiated under the integral sign.

Proof. We have to show that

$$\lim_{h \to 0} \left\{ \frac{F(x+h) - F(x)}{h} - \int_{\alpha}^{\beta} f_x(x,t)dt \right\} = 0. \tag{2}$$

Now, by Taylor's Theorem for two variables*, $f(x+h,t) - f(x,t) = hf_x(x,t) + \frac{1}{2}h^2 f_{xx}(x+\theta h,t)$, where $0 < \theta < 1$. On dividing by h and integrating with respect to t from α to β, we find that

$$\frac{F(x+h) - F(x)}{h} - \int_{\alpha}^{\beta} f_x(x,t)dt = \frac{1}{2}h \int_{\alpha}^{\beta} f_{xx}(x+\theta h,t)dt.$$

The integral on the right-hand does not exceed M, whatever the value of $x + \theta h$. Therefore, as $h \to 0$, the right-hand side tends to zero. This proves (2).

Example 1. Prove that

$$\int_{0}^{\infty} \frac{dx}{(x^2+k)^{n+1}} = \frac{1.3. \ldots (2n-1)}{n!} \pi 2^{-n-1} k^{-\frac{1}{2}-n}, \tag{3}$$

where n is a non-negative integer and k is any positive number.

*See P. J. Hilton, *Partial Derivatives* (in this series), Theorem 4.2 (p. 38) for the case in which $a = x$, $b = y$, $k = 0$.

When $n = 0$, this result reduces to the standard formula

$$\int_0^\infty \frac{dx}{x^2 + k} = k^{-\frac{1}{2}}[\tan^{-1}(xk^{-\frac{1}{2}})]_0^\infty = \frac{1}{2}\pi k^{-\frac{1}{2}}.$$

We differentiate this result n times with respect to k. The roles of t and x in Theorem 2 are now taken by x and k respectively and there is no difficulty in verifying that the conditions of Theorem 2 are satisfied. Indeed, $\dfrac{\partial^n}{\partial k^n}\left\{\dfrac{1}{x^2 + k}\right\}$ behaves like x^{-2n} for large values of x. Thus

$$\int_0^\infty \frac{\partial^n}{\partial k^n}\left\{\frac{1}{x^2 + k}\right\}dx = \frac{\pi}{2}\frac{d^n}{dk^n}(k^{-\frac{1}{2}}),$$

$$(-1)^n n! \int_0^\infty \frac{dx}{(x^2 + k)^{n+1}}$$

$$= \frac{\pi}{2}\left(-\frac{1}{2}\right)\left(-\frac{3}{2}\right)\cdots\left(-\frac{2n-1}{2}\right)k^{-\frac{1}{2}-n},$$

whence (3) follows immediately.

Example 2.

Using the formula $\int_0^\infty e^{-x^2}dx = \frac{1}{2}\sqrt{\pi}$, which will be proved on p. 50, we shall show that, for any value of r,

$$\int_0^\infty e^{-x^2}\cos 2rx\,dx = \frac{1}{2}\sqrt{\pi}e^{-r^2}. \tag{4}$$

Let $I(r) = \int_0^\infty e^{-x^2}\cos 2rx\,dx$. Differentiating with respect

30

3.3 DIFFERENTIATION UNDER INTEGRAL SIGN

to r under the integral sign we obtain that

$$\frac{dI}{dr} = -2 \int_0^\infty e^{-x^2} x \sin 2rx \, dx = \int_0^\infty \frac{d}{dx}(e^{-x^2}) \sin 2rx \, dx$$

$$= [e^{-x^2} \sin 2rx]_0^\infty - 2r \int_0^\infty e^{-x^2} \cos 2rx \, dx.$$

Since the integrated part vanishes at both ends, we have that $dI/dr = -2rI$. The solution of this differential equation is $I(r) = ke^{-r^2}$, where k is a constant. But $I(0) = \frac{1}{2}\sqrt{\pi}$ by the formula quoted above. Hence $k = \frac{1}{2}\sqrt{\pi}$, which proves (4). A more general situation arises when the integrand depends on two or more parameters. For example, a function of two variables is defined by

$$F(x,y) = \int_\alpha^\beta f(x,y,t) dt,$$

and partial differentiation can be carried out under the integral sign, provided that suitable conditions, analogous to those of Theorem 2, are satisfied.

Finally, an integral may be regarded as a function of its upper and lower limit of integration or both, and this variation can occur simultaneously with dependence on a parameter in the integrand. Thus

$$G(x,u,v) = \int_u^v f(x,t) dt$$

is a function of three variables with the following partial derivatives:

$$\frac{\partial G}{\partial x} = \int_u^v f_x(x,t) dt, \quad \frac{\partial G}{\partial v} = f(x,v), \quad \frac{\partial G}{\partial u} = -f(x,u).$$

The last two results follow from the Fundamental Theorem in

31

FUNCTIONS DEFINED BY INTEGRALS

conjunction with the rules for interchanging the limits of integration (equations (15) and (5) of Chapter I).

If u and v are functions of x, the integral

$$H(x) = \int_{u(x)}^{v(x)} f(x,t)dt = G(x,u(x),v(x))$$

again becomes a function of the single variable x, and

$$\frac{dH}{dx} = G_x + G_u u' + G_v v'$$

$$= \int_u^v f_x(x,t)dt - f(x,u)u' + f(x,v)v'. \qquad (5)$$

Example 3. Relative to a function $f(x)$ a sequence of functions $F_1, F_2, \ldots$ is defined by

$$F_n(x) = \int_a^x \frac{(x-t)^{n-1}}{(n-1)!} f(t)dt \quad (n = 1,2,\ldots).$$

Prove that $d^n F_n/dx^n = f$. In other words, F_n is the nth iterated integral of f, subject to the additional conditions that $F_n(a) = 0$. First we observe that $F_1(x) = \int_a^x f(t)dt$, whence $F_1'(x) = f(x)$ by the Fundamental Theorem. Next, if $n \geqq 2$, we use (5) to find the derivative of F_n. Since the last two terms on the right-hand side vanish, we simply have that

$$F_n'(x) = \int_a^x \frac{(x-t)^{n-2}}{(n-2)!} f(t)dt = F_{n-1}(x).$$

The result now follows by induction. For on differentiating the last equation $n-1$ times we obtain that $d^n F_n/dx^n = d^{n-1}F_{n-1}/dx^{n-1}$, and if we assume that $d^{n-1}F_{n-1}/dx^{n-1} = f$, we deduce that $d^n F_n/dx^n = f$, as required.

3.4 INTEGRATION UNDER THE INTEGRAL SIGN

4. INTEGRATION UNDER THE INTEGRAL SIGN

Let us assume that f satisfies the conditions of Theorem 1. This ensures that the function $F(x) = \int_\alpha^\beta f(x,t)dt$ is continuous in $[a,b]$. The integral

$$\int_a^b F(x)dx = \int_a^b \left\{ \int_\alpha^\beta f(x,t)dt \right\}dx \qquad (6)$$

certainly exists; but we should like to know whether the integration can be carried out under the integral sign, that is whether

$$\int_a^b F(x)dx = \int_\alpha^\beta \left\{ \int_a^b f(x,t)dx \right\}dt. \qquad (7)$$

We shall establish (7) under the conditions of Theorem 1 although it must be remarked that less drastic conditions suffice*. It is convenient to write the integrals in (6) and (7) more briefly as $\int_a^b dx \int_\alpha^\beta f(x,t)dt$ and $\int_\alpha^\beta dt \int_a^b f(x,t)dx$ respectively.

Theorem 3. *The function $f(x,t)$ is defined for $a \leq x \leq b$ and $\alpha \leq t \leq \beta$ and satisfies the conditions (i) $|f_x(x,t)| \leq \phi(t)$ for all x and t, and (ii) $\int_\alpha^\beta \phi(t)dt < \infty$. Then*

$$\int_a^b dx \int_\alpha^\beta f(x,t)dt = \int_\alpha^\beta dt \int_a^b f(x,t)dx, \qquad (8)$$

that is the order of integration may be interchanged; in other words, the function $F(x)$, defined in (1), may be integrated under the integral sign.

Proof. As before, put $F(x) = \int_\alpha^\beta f(x,t)dt$. Introduce a variable u which ranges from a to b and define the following functions in

* R. Courant, *loc. cit*, 239.

33

which the constant b has been replaced by the variable u:

$$G(u) = \int_a^u F(x)dx = \int_a^u dx \int_\alpha^\beta f(x,t)dt,$$

$$K(u,t) = \int_a^u f(x,t)dx,$$

$$H(u) = \int_\alpha^\beta K(u,t)dt = \int_\alpha^\beta dt \int_a^u f(x,t)dx.$$

Since F is continuous, we may apply the Fundamental Theorem and deduce that

$$\frac{d}{du}G(u) = F(u).$$

Next we wish to differentiate H with respect to u. According to Theorem 2 this process can be carried out under the integral sign, provided that $|K_{uu}(u,t)| \leqq \phi(t)$ and $\int_\alpha^\beta \phi(t)dt < \infty$. Now, $K_u(u,t) = f(u,t)$ and $K_{uu}(u,t) = f_u(u,t)$. Hence the conditions that have to be satisfied are precisely those which have been postulated in Theorem 3, except that x has been replaced by u. We are therefore justified in writing

$$\frac{d}{du}H(u) = \int_\alpha^\beta K_u(u,t)dt = \int_\alpha^\beta f(u,t)dt = F(u).$$

Thus G and H have the same derivative and can therefore differ only by a constant. However, this constant must be zero, because it is evident from the definitions that $F(a) = H(a) = 0$. We have therefore established that $G(u) = H(u)$ for $a \leqq u \leqq b$. In particular, $G(b) = H(b)$. This last equation is equivalent to (8).

Example 3. Prove that, if $b > a > -1$,

$$\int_0^1 \frac{x^b - x^a}{\log x}dx = \log \frac{b+1}{a+1}.$$

3.4 INTEGRATION UNDER THE INTEGRAL SIGN

We begin with the integral $F(x) = \int_0^1 t^x dt = (1 + x)^{-1}$,

where $x > -1$. On integrating with respect to x from a to b we

find at once that $\int_a^b F(x)dx = \log \dfrac{b + 1}{a + 1}$. On the other hand,

if we carry out the integration under the integral sign, we have
that

$$\int_a^b F(x)dx = \int_0^1 dt \int_a^b t^x dx$$

$$= \int_0^1 dt[t^x/\log t]_a^b = \int_0^1 \frac{t^b - t^a}{\log t} dt.$$

In order to justify the inversion of the order of the two integrations we shall verify that the function $f(x,t) = t^x$ satisfies the conditions of Theorem 3. When $0 \leqq t \leqq 1$ and $x \geqq a$,

$$|f_x(x,t)| = |t^x \log t| \leqq |t^a \log t| = -t^a \log t = \phi(t)$$

and* $\displaystyle\int_0^1 \phi(t)dt = - \int_0^1 t^a \log t\, dt =$

$$= \left[\frac{-t^{a+1}}{a + 1} \log t \right]_0^1 + \int_0^1 \frac{t^a}{a + 1} dt = \frac{1}{(a + 1)^2}$$

Example 4. Consider the function

$$F(x) = \int_0^\pi \log (1 - 2x \cos t + x^2)dt \qquad (9)$$

Evidently $F(0) = 0$. Also $F(-x) = \int_0^\pi \log (1 + 2x \cos t + x^2)dt$.
On changing the variable of integration to $\theta = \pi - t$, we find

---

* In the evaluation of this integral we use the fact that if $\alpha > 0$, $t^\alpha \log t \to 0$, as $t \to 0$. On making the substitution $t = e^{-s}$ it is seen that this is equivalent to stating that $e^{-\alpha s}s \to 0$ as $s \to \infty$, and this follows at once from the remarks on p. 24.

that $F(-x) = \int_0^\pi \log(1 - 2x\cos\theta + x^2)d\theta$, so that $F(-x) = F(x)$. It suffices therefore to examine the function for $x \geq 0$, but we shall in the first place impose the even stronger restriction that $0 \leq x \leq x_0 < 1$, where x_0 is a fixed number less than 1. When x is confined to this range, $1 - 2x\cos t + x^2 \geq (1 - x_0)^2$, which is a fixed positive number. Hence $f(x,t) = \log(1 - 2x\cos t + x^2)$ and its derivatives $f_x, f_{xx}, \ldots$ are continuous functions of t if x lies in the interval $[0, x_0]$. In particular $|f_{xx}| \leq \phi_0$ where ϕ_0 is a suitable constant. It follows that we can apply Theorem 2 to find $F'(x)$. Thus

$$F'(x) = \int_0^\pi \frac{-2\cos t + 2x}{1 - 2x\cos t + x^2} dt.$$

The evaluation of this integral presents no difficulty: when $x = 0$, we have that $F'(0) = \int_0^\pi -2\cos t\, dt = 0$. Next, when $0 < x < x_0$,

$$F'(x) = \frac{1}{x}\left\{ \int_0^\pi dt + (x^2 - 1)\int_0^\pi \frac{dt}{1 - 2x\cos t + x^2}\right\}. \qquad (10)$$

The last integral is evaluated by the substitution $u = \tan\frac{1}{2}t$ and found to be equal to $\pi(1 - x^2)^{-1}$, bearing in mind that, $|x| < 1$. Thus we obtain the rather surprising result that $F'(x) = 0$, if $0 \leq x \leq x_0$. Hence $F(x)$ is constant in $[0, x_0]$ and since $F(0) = 0$, we have in fact that $F = 0$ in this interval. Since x_0 is an arbitrary number between 0 and 1 we have established that

$$F(x) = 0, \text{ if } 0 \leq x < 1.$$

The value of $F(1)$ can be found directly from the definition.

3.4 INTEGRATION UNDER THE INTEGRAL SIGN

In fact, by evaluating the integral in two different ways we find that

$$F(1) = \int_0^\pi \log (2 - 2\cos t)\, dt$$

$$= \int_0^\pi \log (4 \sin^2 \tfrac{1}{2}t)\, dt = 2 \int_0^{\pi/2} \log (4 \sin^2 \theta)\, d\theta$$

and also that

$$F(1) = \int_0^{\pi/2} \log (2 - 2\cos t)\, dt + \int_{\pi/2}^\pi \log (2 - 2\cos t)\, dt$$

$$= \int_0^{\pi/2} \log (2 - 2\cos t)\, dt + \int_0^{\pi/2} \log (2 + 2\cos \theta)\, d\theta$$

$$(t = \pi - \theta)$$

$$= \int_0^{\pi/2} \log \{(2 - 2\cos \theta)(2 + 2\cos \theta)\}\, d\theta$$

$$= \int_0^{\pi/2} \log (4 \sin^2 \theta)\, d\theta.$$

It follows that $F(1) = 2F(1)$, and hence $F(1) = 0$. Finally, if $x > 1$, we put $x = 1/y$ in (9). After a simple calculation it is found that $F(x) = \pi \log x^2 + F(y)$. But $F(y) = 0$ since $0 < y < 1$. Summarising these results we can state that

$$\int_0^\pi \log (1 - 2x \cos t + x^2)\, dt = \begin{cases} 0, & \text{if } |x| \geq 1 \\ \pi \log x^2, & |x| \leq 1. \end{cases} \quad (11)$$

We conclude this chapter by discussing an example in which a somewhat more profound difficulty occurs.

Example 5. When $x > 0$, we deduce from equation (22) of Chapter I that

$$\int_0^\infty e^{-xt} \sin t\, dt = \left[e^{-xt} \frac{-x \sin t - \cos t}{1 + x^2} \right]_0^\infty = \frac{1}{1 + x^2}.$$

This identity may be integrated over the range $[\lambda,\infty]$, where, in the first place, we assume that λ is strictly positive. Thus

$$\int_\lambda^\infty dx \int_0^\infty e^{-xt}\sin t\, dt = \int_\lambda^\infty \frac{dx}{1+x^2} = \tfrac{1}{2}\pi - \tan^{-1}\lambda.$$

We now wish to interchange the order of the integrations by invoking Theorem 2. In the present case $f(x,t) = e^{-xt}\sin t$ and $|f_x(x,t)| = |-t\sin t\, e^{-xt}| \leq te^{-\lambda t}$, because $x > \lambda$ and $t \geq 0$. Since $\int_0^\infty te^{-\lambda t}dt < \infty$, the conditions of Theorem 2 are satisfied and we have that

$$\tfrac{1}{2}\pi - \tan^{-1}\lambda = \int_0^\infty \sin t\, dt \int_\lambda^\infty e^{-xt}dx$$

$$= \int_0^\infty \frac{\sin t}{t}e^{-\lambda t}dt = G(\lambda),$$

say. We emphasise that this equation has been proved only for strictly positive values of λ. But the left-hand side is continuous even at $\lambda = 0$ and tends to $\tfrac{1}{2}\pi$ as $\lambda \to 0$. Let us assume for a moment that the right-hand side is also continuous at $\lambda = 0$. It would then follow that $\lim_{\lambda \to 0+} G(\lambda) = G(0)$ and we should have arrived at the interesting result that

$$\int_0^\infty \frac{\sin t}{t}dt = \frac{\pi}{2} \qquad (12)$$

(which is in fact true). But the continuity of $G(\lambda)$ is not a straightforward consequence of any results we have established in this Chapter, and we prefer to deal with this rather delicate argument in Appendix I, p. 62.

EXERCISES ON CHAPTER THREE

1. From the formula $\int_0^\infty e^{-x^2}\,dx = \frac{1}{2}\sqrt{\pi}$ (equation (24), p. 50) deduce that

$$\int_0^\infty e^{-\lambda x^2}\,dx = \frac{\sqrt{\pi}}{2}\lambda^{-\frac{1}{2}} \text{ and } \int_0^\infty x^2 e^{-\lambda x^2}\,dx = \frac{\sqrt{\pi}}{4}\lambda^{-3/2},$$

where $\lambda > 0$.

2. Show that $\dfrac{d}{dx}\displaystyle\int_{-x}^{x} f(x + t)\,dt = 2f(2x)$.

3. Prove that, if a and b are positive,

(i) $\displaystyle\int_0^\infty \frac{e^{-ax} - e^{-bx}}{x}\,dx = \log\frac{b}{a}$,

(ii) $\displaystyle\int_0^\infty \frac{e^{-ax} - e^{-bx}}{x}\cos rx\,dx = \frac{1}{2}\log\frac{b^2 + r^2}{a^2 + r^2}$

4. Show that $\displaystyle\int_0^\pi \log\frac{1 + a\cos\theta}{1 - a\cos\theta}\frac{d\theta}{\cos\theta} = 2\pi\sin^{-1}a \qquad (|a| < 1)$.

5. Prove that $\displaystyle\int_0^{\pi/2} \log(1 - p\sin^2\theta)\,d\theta = \pi\log\frac{1 + (1 - p)^{\frac{1}{2}}}{2}$, where $0 \leqq p \leqq 1$. Hence, or otherwise, show that

$$\int_0^{\pi/2} \log(\sin x)\,dx = \int_0^{\pi/2} \log(\cos x)\,dx = -\frac{1}{2}\pi\log 2.$$

6. Show that $\displaystyle\int_0^\infty \frac{\sin \alpha x}{x}\,dx$ is equal to $\frac{1}{2}\pi$ if $\alpha > 0$, and is equal to $-\frac{1}{2}\pi$ if $\alpha < 0$.

7. Prove that $\displaystyle\int_0^\infty \left(\frac{\sin x}{x}\right)^2\,dx = \frac{1}{2}\pi$.

8. Prove that $\int_0^\infty \log\left(1 + \dfrac{a^2}{x^2}\right) dx = \pi a$, if $a > 0$.

CHAPTER FOUR

The Factorial (Gamma) Function

1. EULER'S SECOND INTEGRAL

The reader will be familiar with the function

$$n! = 1 \cdot 2 \cdot 3 \cdot \ldots \cdot n, \tag{1}$$

which is defined for every positive integer n. In order to render the general rule

$$(n + 1)! = (n + 1)n! \tag{2}$$

still valid when $n = 0$, it is customary to put

$$0! = 1.$$

But there seems to be no obvious way of extending the definition to fractional or negative values of n by simple devices of this kind. Yet it is important to construct a function, $F(x)$, which for non-negative integral values of x agrees with $n!$, that is, which has the property that

$$F(n) = n! \quad (n = 0,1,2, \ldots), \tag{3}$$

and is reasonably well behaved for other values of x.

We can translate the problem into geometrical language as follows: plot the points

$$(0,0!), (1,1!), (2,2!), \ldots, (n,n!), \ldots \tag{4}$$

in the (x,y)-plane (for the sake of simplicity we confine ourselves to non-negative values of x). Since the factorial function grows very rapidly, the scale on the y-axis in Fig. 3 has been made very much smaller than that on the x-axis.

D   41

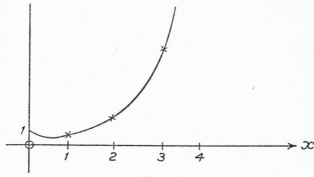

Figure 3.

We now wish to draw a smooth curve through the points (4), whose equation $y = F(x)$ corresponds to the function we are looking for.

It is clear from the outset that there can be no unique solution. For if $F(x)$ satisfies (3) so does $F(x)\cos 2\pi m x$, where m is any integer whatsoever, and many other solutions could be constructed. Thus among the possible solutions we shall endeavour to find one that has other convenient properties.

The most important solution can be presented in what is called *Euler's Second Integral*, namely

$$F(x) = \int_0^\infty t^x e^{-t} dt \qquad (5)$$

We have seen on p. 27 that this integral exists for $x > -1$, and Theorem 1 (p. 28) implies that $F(x)$ is continuous in this range. On integrating by parts we find that

$$F(x + 1) = \int_0^\infty t^{x+1} e^{-t} dt$$
$$= \left[-t^{x+1} e^{-t} \right]_0^\infty + (x + 1) \int_0^\infty t^x e^{-t} dt.$$

42

Since $x + 1 > 0$, it follows that $t^{x+1}e^{-t} \to 0$ as $t \to \infty$. Hence

$$F(x + 1) = (x + 1)F(x), \quad (x > -1), \qquad (6)$$

which generalises the functional equation (2) to a continuous variable. By a repeated application of (6) to the case in which $x = n - 1$ is a positive integer, we deduce that

$$F(n) = nF(n - 1) = n(n - 1)F(n - 2)$$
$$= \ldots = n(n - 1)(n - 2) \ldots 3 \cdot 2 \cdot F(1).$$

Finally, by a straightforward use of the definition, we find that

$$F(1) = \int_0^\infty te^{-t}dt = [-te^{-t}]_0^\infty$$
$$+ \int_0^\infty e^{-t}dt = [-te^{-t} - e^{-t}]_0^\infty = 1.$$

Hence $F(n) = n!$, as required. This proves that (5) is a solution. Henceforth we shall simply write $x!$ in place of $F(x)$, that is we define

$$x! = \int_0^\infty t^x e^{-t}dt \quad (x > -1) \qquad (7)$$

which agrees with the customary meaning of the factorial function when x is a non-negative integer. In some contexts it is a little more convenient to use instead the Γ-function (Gamma function) defined by

$$\Gamma(x) = \int_0^\infty t^{x-1} e^{-t}dt \quad (x > 0). \qquad (8)$$

The two functions are evidently related by the equation

$$\Gamma(x+1) = x!, \qquad (9)$$

so that passing from one function to the other involves only a slight change of notation. The *functional equations for $x!$ and $F(x)$* take the form

$$(x + 1)! = (x + 1)x! \quad (x > -1) \qquad (10)$$

43

THE FACTORIAL (GAMMA) FUNCTION

and
$$\Gamma(x + 1) = x\Gamma(x) \quad (x > 0) \tag{11}$$
respectively.

We generally prefer the factorial function, but occasionally a formula looks neater when expressed in terms of the Γ-function. The integrals by which the functions were originally defined, can be transformed into different guises by changing the variable of integration. For example, if we put $t = u^2$,

$$x! = 2 \int_0^\infty e^{-u^2} u^{2x+1} du \quad (x > -1). \tag{12}$$

In particular,

$$(-\tfrac{1}{2})! = 2 \int_0^\infty e^{-u^2} du. \tag{13}$$

Like other important functions of mathematical analysis, the function $x!$ has been well tabulated. For references see Jahnke-Emde, *Tables of Functions*, Berlin 1933, p. 86-95.

In Fig. 4 the curve $f(x) = x!$ is sketched for the interval $-1 < x \leqq 3$.

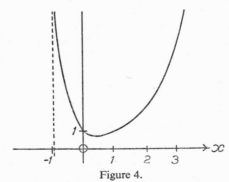

Figure 4.

In virtue of the functional equation it is evidently sufficient to tabulate the values of $x!$ in an interval of length 1, say when

$0 < x < 1$. For example, from tables $(0 \cdot 3)! = 0 \cdot 8975$. Hence by (10), $(1 \cdot 3)! = (1 \cdot 3)(0 \cdot 3)! = 1 \cdot 1668$. Again, $(0 \cdot 3)! = (0 \cdot 3)(-0 \cdot 7)!$, whence $(-0 \cdot 7)! = 0 \cdot 8975/0 \cdot 3 = 2 \cdot 992$.

By a repeated application of the functional equation we have that

$$(x + n)! = (x + n)(x + n - 1) \dots (x + 1)x \, x!, \quad (14)$$

where n is any positive integer. Solving for $x!$ we can write

$$x! = \frac{(x + n)!}{(x + n)(x + n - 1) \dots (x + 1)}. \quad (15)$$

This equation could be used to define $x!$ for all negative values of x, except for negative integers. In fact

$$\lim_{x \to -n} x! = \infty \text{ or } -\infty,$$

according as x approaches $-n$ from the right or from the left.

2. THE BETA FUNCTION

This function, which is also known as *Euler's First Integral*, is defined as

$$B(x,y) = \int_0^1 t^{x-1}(1 - t)^{y-1} dt \quad (x > 0, \, y > 0), \quad (16)$$

where B is a capital Beta, not a B. The integral is an improper integral when $0 < x < 1$ or $0 < y < 1$; its existence has been established in Example 3 (p. 21).

On changing the variable of integration by the substitution $t = 1 - u$, we find that $B(x,y) = -\int_1^0 (1 - u)^{x-1} u^{y-1} du = \int_0^1 u^{y-1}(1 - u)^{x-1} du$. Thus

$$B(x,y) = B(y,x), \quad (17)$$

that is, the B-function is symmetrical with respect to its two variables. Next, in the definition (16) put $t = v/1 + v$, and hence $1 - t = (1 + v)^{-1}$, $dt = (1 + v)^{-2}dv (0 \leq v < \infty)$. This gives an alternative form for the B-function, namely

$$B(x,y) = \int_0^\infty \left(\frac{v}{v+1}\right)^{x-1} \left(\frac{1}{1+v}\right)^{y-1} \frac{dv}{(1+v)^2},$$

$$B(x,y) = \int_0^\infty \frac{v^{x-1}}{(1+v)^{x+y}} \, dv. \tag{18}$$

Another useful expression for the B-function is obtained by the substitution

$$t = \sin^2\theta, 1 - t = \cos^2\theta, dt = 2\cos\theta\sin\theta, 0 \leq \theta \leq \pi/2,$$

which yields the formula

$$B(x,y) = 2\int_0^{\pi/2} (\sin\theta)^{2x-1}(\cos\theta)^{2y-1}d\theta \quad (x > 0, y > 0). \tag{19}$$

Example 1.

$$B(\tfrac{1}{2},\tfrac{1}{2}) = 2\int_0^{\pi/2} d\theta = \pi.$$

On putting $x = y$ in (19) we find that

$$B(x,x) = 2\int_0^{\pi/2} (\sin\theta\cos\theta)^{2x-1}d\theta$$

$$= 2^{-2x+1}\int_0^{\pi/2} (\sin 2\theta)^{2x-1}d(2\theta)$$

$$= 2^{-2x+1}\int_0^{\pi} (\sin\phi)^{2x+1}d\phi$$

$$= 2^{-2x+2}\int_0^{\pi/2} (\sin\phi)^{2x-1}d\phi.$$

Thus

$$B(x,x) = 2^{-2x+1}B(x,\tfrac{1}{2}). \tag{20}$$

There is an interesting formula which expresses the B-function in terms of the factorial function, namely

$$\int_0^1 t^x(1-t)^y dt = \mathrm{B}(x+1, y+1) =$$

$$= \frac{x!\, y!}{(x+y+1)!} \quad (x > -1, y > -1). \qquad (21)$$

In view of this relation, the B-function may be regarded as little more than a convenient abbreviation. Let us use the temporary notation

$$C(x,y) = \frac{x!\, y!}{(x+y+1)!}.$$

It is required to prove that

$$C(x,y) = \mathrm{B}(x+1, y+1) \quad (x > -1, y > -1). \qquad (22)$$

First, we remark that B satisfies the recurrence relations

$$\mathrm{B}(x+2, y+1) = \frac{x+1}{x+y+2}\mathrm{B}(x+1, y+1),$$

$$\mathrm{B}(x+1, y+2) = \frac{y+1}{x+y+2}\mathrm{B}(x+1, y+1).$$

For reasons of symmetry it is evidently sufficient to prove the first of these equations. From (16) we have that

$$\mathrm{B}(x+2, y+1) = \int_0^1 t^{x+1}(1-t)^y dt$$

$$= \left[-\frac{1}{y+1}t^{x+1}(1-t)^{y+1} \right]_0^1 + \frac{x+1}{y+1}\int_0^1 t^x(1-t)^{y+1}dt$$

$$= \frac{x+1}{y+1}\int_0^1 t^x(1-t)(1-t)^y dt$$

$$= \frac{x+1}{y+1}\mathrm{B}(x+1, y+1) - \frac{x+1}{y+1}\mathrm{B}(x+2, y+1),$$

whence

$$(x + y + 2)B(x + 2, y + 1) = (x + 1)B(x + 1, y + 1).$$

Now the function C satisfies a similar pair of relations, namely

$$C(x + 1, y) = \frac{x + 1}{x + y + 2} C(x, y),$$

$$C(x, y + 1) = \frac{y + 1}{x + y + 2} C(x, y),$$

which are immediate consequences of (10). It is therefore sufficient to prove that

$$C(x + m - 1, y + n - 1) = B(x + m, y + n),$$

where m and n are arbitrary positive integers; for by a repeated use of the recurrence relations this last equation can be reduced to (22). Alternatively, we may say that (22) need only be established for sufficiently great values of x and y. In our case it will be convenient to assume that $x \geqq 2$ and $y \geqq 2$. Starting from the definition (7) we can write

$$x! y! = \left(\int_0^\infty u^x e^{-u} du \right) \left(\int_0^\infty v^y e^{-y} dv \right)$$

$$= \int_0^\infty du \int_0^\infty u^x v^y e^{-(u+v)} dv.$$

In the inner integral we make the substitution $v = tu$, regarding t as the new variable of integration and u as constant. Thus

$$x! y! = \int_0^\infty du \int_0^\infty u^{x+y+1} t^y e^{-(1+t)u} du$$

$$= \int_0^\infty du \int_0^\infty f(u, t) dt,$$

where $f(u, t) = u^{x+y+1} t^y e^{-(1+t)u}$.

We now wish to interchange the order of integration by invoking Theorem 3 of Chapter III. For this purpose we have to examine the absolute value of the partial derivative

$$f_u(u,t) = t^y\{(x + y + 1)u^{x+y}e^{-(1+t)u}$$
$$- u^{x+y+1}(1 + t)e^{-(1+t)u}\}. \qquad (23)$$

Now it is easy to show, by the usual methods of the Differential Calculus, that, when α and β are positive constants and u is a positive variable, the function $u^\alpha e^{-\beta u}$ attains its maximum when $u = \alpha/\beta$ and that accordingly its greatest value is $(\alpha/\beta)^\alpha e^{-\alpha}$. Applying this result to each of the two terms on the right-hand side of (23) and adding them, we find that

$$\left|f_u(u,t)\right| < t^y\{(x + y + 1)\left(\frac{x + y}{1 + t}\right)^{x+y} e^{-x-y}$$

$$+ (1 + t)\left(\frac{x + y + 1}{1 + t}\right)^{x+y+1} e^{-x-y-1}\},$$

that is

$$\left|f_u(u,t)\right| \leqq Kt^y(1 + t)^{-x-y},$$

where K depends on x and y, but not on t. Since

$$\int_0^\infty t^y(1 + t)^{-x-y}dt < \infty,$$

it follows that the inversion of the order of the integrations is justified. Thus

$$x!y! = \int_0^\infty dt \int_0^\infty u^{x+y+1}t^y e^{-(1+t)u}du.$$

THE FACTORIAL (GAMMA) FUNCTION

Finally, on making the substitution $s = (1 + t)u$, we obtain that

$$x! y! = \int_0^\infty dt \int_0^\infty \frac{s^{x+y+1}}{(1+t)^{x+y+1}} t^y e^{-s} \frac{ds}{1+t}$$

$$= \int_0^\infty \frac{t^y dt}{(1+t)^{x+y+2}} \int_0^\infty s^{x+y+1} e^{-s} ds$$

$$= (x + y + 1)! \, B(x + 1, y + 1). \quad \text{by (18)}$$

This proves (21).

Example 2. Apply (21) to the case in which $x = y = -\frac{1}{2}$, and use Example 1. Thus

$$\pi = \frac{((-\tfrac{1}{2})!)^2}{0!}$$

and hence

$$(-\tfrac{1}{2})! = \sqrt{\pi} = 2 \int_0^\infty e^{-u^2} du; \quad (\tfrac{1}{2})! = \tfrac{1}{2}\sqrt{\pi}. \quad (24)$$

Example 3. Compare the formulae (19) and (21), putting $2x + 1 = m$, $2y + 1 = n$. This yields the interesting result that

$$\int_0^{\pi/2} \sin^m\theta \cos^n\theta \, d\theta$$

$$= \tfrac{1}{2} \frac{\dfrac{m-1}{2}! \, \dfrac{n-1}{2}!}{\dfrac{m+n!}{2}} \quad (m > -1, n > -1). \quad (25)$$

When m and n are positive integers, the integral can be evaluated by the reduction method referred to in Chapter I (see

Equation (17), p. 13). It is instructive to check this result in a simple case. Take $m = 6, n = 0$. Then

$$\int_0^{\pi/2} \sin^6\theta \, d\theta = \tfrac{1}{2}(\tfrac{5}{2})! \, (-\tfrac{1}{2})! \, / 3! = \tfrac{1}{2}\tfrac{5}{2} \cdot \tfrac{3}{2} \cdot \tfrac{1}{2}((-\tfrac{1}{2})!)^2 / 3!$$

$$= \frac{5 \cdot 3 \cdot 1}{6 \cdot 4 \cdot 2}\frac{\pi}{2},$$

in agreement with formula (20) of p. 14. Next, replace x by $x + 1$ in (20) of p. 46 and compare it with (21). Then

$$\frac{(x!)^2}{(2x + 1)!} = 2^{-2x-1}\frac{x!(-\tfrac{1}{2})!}{(x + \tfrac{1}{2})!},$$

$$\frac{x!}{(2x + 1)(2x)!} = \frac{2^{-2x-1}\sqrt{\pi}}{(x + \tfrac{1}{2})(x - \tfrac{1}{2})!},$$

$$(2x)! = \frac{2^{2x}}{\sqrt{\pi}}x!(x - \tfrac{1}{2})!. \tag{26}$$

This result is known as the *duplication formula* for the factorial function. Finally, when $0 < x < 1$, we may put $y = -x$ in (21). Then

$$x!(-x)! = B(1 + x, 1 - x)$$

and by (18), followed by integration by parts,

$$B(1 + x, 1 - x) = \int_0^\infty \frac{v^x}{(1 + v)^2}dv = x \int_0^\infty \frac{v^{x-1}}{1 + v}dv.$$

Now it is known, but rather difficult to prove, that

$$\int_0^\infty \frac{v^{x-1}}{1 + v}dv = \frac{\pi}{\sin\pi x} \quad (0 < x < 1). \tag{27}$$

This result is usually established by means of contour integration in the complex plane, or else by an appeal to the partial fraction development of cosec x. A more elementary, but somewhat tedious proof of (27), is sketched in Appendix II. Assuming this result, we have that

$$x!(-x)! = \pi x/\sin\pi x \qquad (0 < x < 1). \qquad (28)$$

Since this formula may be used to define $x!$ for negative values of x, it is sometimes called the *extension formula* of the factorial function.

Example 4. Applying (21) we find that

$$\int_0^1 t^{\frac{1}{3}}(1-t)^{\frac{2}{3}}dt = \frac{\frac{1}{3}!\,\frac{2}{3}!}{2!} = \frac{\frac{1}{3}!\,\frac{2}{3}(-\frac{1}{3}!)}{2} = \frac{1}{3}\,\frac{1}{3}!\,(-\frac{1}{3}!),$$

whence by (28),

$$\int_0^1 t^{\frac{1}{3}}(1-t)^{\frac{2}{3}}dt = \frac{1}{3}\frac{\pi}{3}\bigg/\sin\frac{\pi}{3} = \frac{2\pi}{9\sqrt{3}}$$

3. THE PRODUCT EXPANSION OF $x!$

We consider the integral

$$F(x,n) = \int_0^n t^x\left(1 - \frac{t}{n}\right)^n dt \qquad (x > -1). \qquad (29)$$

Since $\lim_{n\to\infty}\left(1 - \frac{t}{n}\right)^n = e^{-t}$, it is reasonable to expect that

$$\lim_{n\to\infty} F(x,n) = \int_0^\infty t^x e^{-t}dt = x!. \qquad (30)$$

This is in fact true, but a more rigorous argument must be given, and this will be presented in Appendix III. In the meantime, let us accept (30) and evaluate (29) in a different way.

4.3 THE PRODUCT EXPANSION OF $x!$

On changing the variable of integration by the substitution $t = nu$ and using (21) we find that

$$F(x,n) = \int_0^1 n^{x+1} u^x (1 - u)^n du$$

$$= n^{x+1} \frac{x!\, n!}{(n + x + 1)!} = \frac{n}{n + x + 1} \frac{n^x x!\, n!}{(n + x)!}.$$

Since $\lim\limits_{n \to \infty} \dfrac{n}{n + x + 1} = 1$, we deduce from (30) that

$$x! = \lim_{n \to \infty} F(x,n) = \lim_{n \to \infty} \frac{n^x x!\, n!}{(n + x)!}.$$ Substituting for $(n + x)!$ from

(15) and cancelling $x!$ once, we obtain Gauss's *product formula* for the factorial function, namely

$$x! = \lim_{n \to \infty} \frac{n^x n!}{(x + 1)(x + 2) \dots (x + n)}. \qquad (31)$$

Although this result has been derived under the assumption that $x > -1$, it can in fact be used to define $x!$ for all values of x other than negative integers. Combining (31) with (28) we obtain the product expansion of $\sin \pi x$, namely

$$\sin \pi x = \frac{\pi x}{x!(-x!)}$$

$$= \lim_{n \to \infty} \pi x (1^2 - x^2)(2^2 - x^2) \dots (n^2 - x^2)/(n!)^2,$$

which is usually written as an infinite product, namely,

$$\sin \pi x = \pi x \prod_{k=1}^{\infty} \left(1 - \frac{x^2}{k^2}\right). \qquad (32)$$

From (31) we shall derive a product expansion for $1/x!$, which is due to Weierstrass. Writing n^x in the form $e^{x \log n}$ and taking the reciprocal of (31) we find that

$$\frac{1}{x!} = \lim_{n \to \infty} e^{-x \log n} \left(1 + \frac{x}{1}\right)\left(1 + \frac{x}{2}\right) \cdots \left(1 + \frac{x}{n}\right).$$

Put $\gamma_n = \left(1 + \frac{1}{2} + \ldots + \frac{1}{n}\right) - \log n$, then it is known

that $\gamma_n \to \gamma$, where γ is Euler's constant (see J. A. Green, *Sequences and Series*, p. 43).

Hence

$$\frac{1}{x!} = \lim_{n \to \infty} e^{x\gamma_n} \prod_{k=1}^{n} \left(1 + \frac{x}{k}\right) e^{-x/k},$$

that is

$$\frac{1}{x!} = e^{\gamma x} \prod_{k=1}^{\infty} \left(1 + \frac{x}{k}\right) e^{-x/k}. \tag{33}$$

This formula makes it plain that the function $1/x!$ vanishes when x is a negative integer.

The next three results are derived from (33) by a formal procedure which would present no difficulty if the product on the right were to involve only a finite number of factors. But for infinite products these steps are not always legitimate, and the gap in the argument is filled in Appendix IV.

Taking logarithms on both sides of (33) we find that

$$\log x! = -\gamma x + \sum_{k=1}^{\infty} \left\{\frac{x}{k} - \log\left(1 + \frac{x}{k}\right)\right\},$$

whence on differentiating term by term

$$\frac{d}{dx} \log x! = \frac{(x!)'}{x!} = -\gamma + \sum_{k=1}^{\infty} \left(\frac{1}{k} - \frac{1}{x+k} \right), \quad (34)$$

and by a further differentiation

$$\frac{d^2}{dx^2} \log x! = \sum_{k=1}^{\infty} \frac{1}{(x+k)^2}. \quad (35)$$

Example 5. $\left(\frac{d}{dx} x! \right)_{x=0} = -\gamma$. This follows at once from (34) on putting $x = 0$ and remembering that $0! = 1$.

From the formula (35) it is obvious that $\frac{d^2}{dx^2} \log x!$ is always positive when $x > -1$, but in view of later applications it is desirable to have more precise bounds for this function. This is accomplished by comparing the infinite series (35) with the integral $\int_1^{\infty} (x+t)^{-2} dt$. However, it will now be necessary to assume that $x > 0$. For a fixed positive value of x we clearly have that

$$\left. \begin{array}{l} (x+k)^{-2} < (x+t)^{-2}, \text{ when } k-1 \leqq t \leqq k \\ (x+k)^{-2} > (x+t)^{-2}, \text{ when } k \leqq t \leqq k+1 \end{array} \right\} (k = 1, 2, \ldots),$$

whence on integrating,

$$\int_k^{k+1} (x+t)^{-2} dt < (x+k)^{-2} < \int_{k-1}^{k} (x+t)^{-2} dt.$$

Hence, on summing over k,

$$\frac{1}{x+1} = \int_1^\infty (x+t)^{-2}dt < \sum_{k=1}^\infty (x+k)^{-2}$$

$$< \int_0^\infty (x+t)^{-2}dt = \frac{1}{x}.$$

Thus

$$\frac{1}{x+1} < \frac{d^2}{dx^2}\log x! < \frac{1}{x} \quad (x > 0). \tag{36}$$

4. STIRLING'S FORMULA

As the reader may be aware, the function $x!$ increases very rapidly with x, and even in the simplest case, when x is a positive integer, it is hardly practicable to write down the exact value of $x!$. It is therefore desirable to have, what is called, an *asymptotic expression* for $x!$ that is a function $\sigma(x)$ such that

$$\frac{x!}{\sigma(x)} \to 1, \text{ as } x \to \infty,$$

(and where $\sigma(x)$ is easier to compute than $x!$). Such a function was found by Stirling about 1730, apart from a constant factor (see equation (41)).

For technical reasons it is preferable to obtain first an asymptotic expression for the function

$$L(x) = \log x!.$$

We consider the integral

$$J(\alpha) = \int_{\alpha-1}^\alpha L(x)dx \quad (\alpha > 0).$$

On differentiating with respect to α (see (5) p. 32) we find that

$$J'(\alpha) = L(\alpha) - L(\alpha - 1) = \log \frac{\alpha!}{(\alpha - 1)!} = \log \alpha,$$

whence on integrating

$$J(\alpha) = \alpha \log \alpha - \alpha + c,$$

where c is a constant. On replacing α by $\alpha + \frac{1}{2}$ we obtain that

$$J(\alpha + \tfrac{1}{2}) = \int_{\alpha - \frac{1}{2}}^{\alpha + \frac{1}{2}} L(x)dx = \int_{-\frac{1}{2}}^{\frac{1}{2}} L(\alpha + t)dt. \qquad (38)$$

We are interested in finding an expression for $L(\alpha)$ when α is large. This will be done by expanding both sides of (38) and arranging the terms in decreasing order of magnitude. Terms down to constant terms will have to be recorded in detail, but terms of the order α^{-1} need not be known precisely, as they will tend to zero as α tends to infinity. These terms will be collectively denoted by the symbol $O(\alpha^{-1})$, which stands for any function having the property that $|\alpha O(\alpha^{-1})|$ remains bounded as α tends to infinity.

On the left of (38) we have

$$J(\alpha + \tfrac{1}{2}) = (\alpha + \tfrac{1}{2}) \log (\alpha + \tfrac{1}{2}) - (\alpha + \tfrac{1}{2}) + c$$

$$= (\alpha + \tfrac{1}{2}) \left\{ \log \alpha + \log \left(1 + \frac{1}{2\alpha} \right) \right\} - (\alpha + \tfrac{1}{2}) + c$$

$$= (\alpha + \tfrac{1}{2}) \left\{ \log \alpha + \left(\frac{1}{2\alpha} - \frac{1}{8\alpha^2} + \cdots \right) \right\} - (\alpha + \tfrac{1}{2}) + c,$$

whence

$$J(\alpha + \tfrac{1}{2}) = (\alpha + \tfrac{1}{2}) \log \alpha - \alpha + c + O(\alpha^{-1}). \qquad (39)$$

Next, by Taylor's Theorem,

$$L(\alpha + t) = L(\alpha) + tL'(\alpha) + \tfrac{1}{2}t^2 L''(\xi),$$

$$\text{where } \alpha - \tfrac{1}{2} < \xi < \alpha + \tfrac{1}{2}.$$

E

On integrating this equation we obtain that

$$J(\alpha + \tfrac{1}{2}) = \int_{-\frac{1}{2}}^{\frac{1}{2}} \{L(\alpha) + tL'(\alpha) + \tfrac{1}{2}t^2 L''(\xi)\}dt$$

$$= L(\alpha) + \tfrac{1}{2}\int_{-\frac{1}{2}}^{\frac{1}{2}} t^2 L''(\xi)dt,$$

the second term being zero, because $\int_{-\frac{1}{2}}^{\frac{1}{2}} t\, dt = 0$. We use (36) to find an estimate for the last integral.

Thus

$$0 < \tfrac{1}{2}\int_{-\frac{1}{2}}^{\frac{1}{2}} t^2 L''(\xi)dt < \tfrac{1}{2}\int_{-\frac{1}{2}}^{\frac{1}{2}} t^2 \xi^{-1} dt$$

$$< (\alpha - \tfrac{1}{2})^{-1}\tfrac{1}{2}\int_{-\frac{1}{2}}^{\frac{1}{2}} t^2 dt = \frac{1}{24}(\alpha - \tfrac{1}{2})^{-1}.$$

Hence we are justified in stating that

$$\tfrac{1}{2}\int_{-\frac{1}{2}}^{\frac{1}{2}} t^2 L''(\xi)dt = O(\alpha^{-1}).$$

It now follows from (39) that

$$L(\alpha) = J(\alpha + \tfrac{1}{2}) + O(\alpha^{-1})$$

$$= (\alpha + \tfrac{1}{2}) \log \alpha - \alpha + c + O(\alpha^{-1}). \quad (40)$$

It remains to find c; this is a somewhat delicate task, which was in fact accomplished only after Stirling's time. Let us take logarithms of the duplication formula (26) of p. 51, and then put $x = \alpha$. Thus

$$L(2\alpha) = 2\alpha \log 2 - \tfrac{1}{2} \log \pi + L(\alpha) + L(\alpha - \tfrac{1}{2}).$$

Substitute for L from (40) on both sides of this equation. This yields $(2\alpha + \tfrac{1}{2}) \log 2\alpha - 2\alpha + c = 2\alpha \log 2 - \tfrac{1}{2} \log \pi + (\alpha + \tfrac{1}{2}) \log \alpha - \alpha + c + \alpha \log (\alpha - \tfrac{1}{2}) - \alpha + \tfrac{1}{2} + c + O(\alpha^{-1}).$

Note that $\alpha \log (\alpha - \frac{1}{2}) = \alpha \left\{ \log \alpha + \log \left(1 - \frac{1}{2\alpha} \right) \right\} =$
$\alpha \left\{ \log \alpha - \frac{1}{2\alpha} - \ldots \right\} = \alpha \log \alpha - \frac{1}{2} + O(\alpha^{-1}).$

After a short elementary calculation it is found that
$$c = \tfrac{1}{2} \log 2\pi. \qquad (41)$$

We have now obtained the complete result, namely,
$$\log \alpha! = (\alpha + \tfrac{1}{2}) \log \alpha - \alpha + \tfrac{1}{2} \log 2\pi + O(\alpha^{-1}), \qquad (42)$$
or on taking exponentials,
$$\alpha! = (2\pi\alpha)^{\frac{1}{2}}(\alpha/e)^{\alpha} \exp \{ O(\alpha^{-1}) \}.$$

This implies that
$$\lim_{\alpha \to \infty} \frac{\alpha!}{(2\pi\alpha)^{\frac{1}{2}}(\alpha/e)^{\alpha}} = 1. \qquad (43)$$

The last result is usually written briefly as
$$\alpha! \sim (2\pi\alpha)^{\frac{1}{2}}(\alpha/e)^{\alpha} \qquad (44)$$

and is referred to as *Stirling's formula*, especially when α is a positive integer.

More precisely we can express the meaning of (44) by saying that
$$\alpha! = (2\pi\alpha)^{\frac{1}{2}}(\alpha/e)^{\alpha}\rho(\alpha), \qquad (45)$$
where $\rho(\alpha) \to 1$ as $\alpha \to \infty$.

The approximation to $\alpha!$ by the function
$$\sigma(\alpha) = (2\pi\alpha)^{\frac{1}{2}} (\alpha/e)^{\alpha}$$
is surprisingly good even for moderately great values of α, as is illustrated by the short table below:

α	$\log \alpha!$	$\log \sigma(\alpha)$	$\alpha!/\sigma(\alpha)$
10	6·5598	6·5562	1·0078
20	18·3861	18·3844	1·0039
30	32·4236	32·4225	1·0026

THE FACTORIAL (GAMMA) FUNCTION

EXERCISES ON CHAPTER FOUR

1. Prove that

$$\mathrm{B}(x,y) = \int_0^1 \frac{t^{p-1} + t^{q-1}}{(1+t)^{p+q}} dt = \tfrac{1}{2} \int_0^\infty \frac{s^{p-1} + s^{q-1}}{(1+s)^{p+q}} ds \quad (x > 0, y > 0).$$

2. Show that

(i) $\displaystyle\int_1^\infty x^{-5}(x-1)^{3/2}dx = 3\pi/128$,   (ii) $\displaystyle\int_0^4 x^2(4-x)^{3/2}dx = 2^{13}/315$.

3. Prove that   (i) $\displaystyle\int_0^1 \frac{x^{p-1}(1-x)^{q-1}}{(ax+b)^{p+q}}dx$

$$= (a+b)^{-p}b^{-q}\mathrm{B}(p,q) \quad (p > 0 \; q > 0, a+b \neq 0, b \neq 0).$$

(ii) $\displaystyle\int_{-1}^1 (1+x)^r(1-x)^s dx = 2^{r+s+1} r! s!/(r+s+1)! \quad (r > -1, s > -1).$

(iii) $\displaystyle\int_0^{\pi/2} \cos^{2x-1}\theta \sin^{2y-1}\theta (a\cos^2\theta + b\sin^2\theta)^{-x-y}d\theta = \tfrac{1}{2}a^{-x}b^{-y}\mathrm{B}(x,y)$

           $(a,b,x,y \text{ positive constants}).$

4. Show that $\displaystyle\int_a^b x(x-a)^{-\alpha}(b-x)^{\alpha-1}dx$

$$= \frac{\pi}{\sin \pi\alpha} \{\alpha a + (1-\alpha)b\} \quad (0 < \alpha < 1, b > a).$$

5. Prove that $\displaystyle\int_0^1 (1-x^4)^{-\frac{1}{2}}dx = \left(\frac{8}{\pi}\right)^{\frac{1}{2}} \{(\tfrac{1}{4})!\}^2.$

6. Prove that (i) $\displaystyle\lim_{n\to\infty} \frac{n^x n!}{(n+x)!} = 1$,   (ii) $\Gamma(x) = \displaystyle\lim_{n\to\infty} n^x \mathrm{B}(x,n).$

7. Show that $\displaystyle\int_0^\infty \frac{\cosh\alpha x}{\cosh x}dx = \frac{\pi}{2\cos(\tfrac{1}{2}\alpha\pi)} \quad (-1 < \alpha < 1).$

EXERCISES

8. Prove that $\lim\limits_{n \to \infty} (\pi n)^{\frac{1}{2}} 2^{-2n} \binom{2n}{n} = 1$ and deduce* that

$$\frac{\pi}{2} = \lim\limits_{n \to \infty} \frac{2.2.4.4.6.6 \dots \quad 2n.2n}{1.3.3.5.5.7 \dots (2n-1)(2n+1)}.$$

(*Wallis's Product*).

* For an elementary proof of this result see e.g. R. Courant, *Differential and Integral Calculus*, (Blackie and Son Ltd.), vol. 1, p. 224.

Appendix I

The gap left in the proof of equation (12) on p. 38 amounts to the assertion that

$$\lim_{\lambda \to 0+} \int_0^\infty \frac{\sin t}{t} e^{-\lambda t} dt = \int_0^\infty \frac{\sin t}{t} dt, \qquad (1)$$

the existence of the integral on the right having been previously established (p. 22). Equation (1) is equivalent to

$$\lim_{\lambda \to 0+} \int_0^\infty \sin t \, \frac{1 - e^{-\lambda t}}{t} dt = 0$$

or, on putting $\lambda t = s$, to

$$\lim_{\lambda \to 0} \int_0^\infty \sin(s/\lambda) \frac{1 - e^{-s}}{s} ds = 0. \qquad (2)$$

This will be an immediate consequence of the following

Lemma*: *Let $\phi(s)$ be a function such that* (i) $\lim_{s \to \infty} \phi(s) = 0$, (ii) $\phi'(s)$ *exists for* $s \geq 0$ *and* (iii) $\int_0^\infty |\phi'(s)| ds < \infty$. *Then* $\lim_{\lambda \to 0} \int_0^\infty \sin(s/\lambda) \, \phi(s) ds = 0$.

Proof: Integrating by parts we have that

$$\int_0^\infty \sin(s/\lambda) \, \phi(s) ds$$

$$= [-\lambda \cos(s/\lambda) \, \phi(s)]_0^\infty + \lambda \int_0^\infty \cos(s/\lambda) \, \phi'(s) ds,$$

---

* This is a weak form of what is usually known as the *Riemann-Lebesgue Lemma*.

where the existence of the last integral is an immediate consequence of condition (iii) and the first term on the right reduces to $\lambda\phi(0)$. This proves that the integral on the left exists, although, strictly speaking, we should have taken as the upper limit a variable which is made to tend to infinity. Moreover, if

$$\int_0^\infty |\phi'(s)|\,ds = M, \text{ then } \left| \int_0^\infty \sin(s/\lambda)\phi(s)\,ds \right| < |\lambda|\{\phi(0) + M\},$$

whence the result follows by letting λ tend to zero.

It is not difficult to verify that the function $\phi(s) = (1 - e^{-s})/s$ satisfies the condition of the Lemma (see example 5, p. 22). This establishes (2).

Appendix II

It is our aim to establish the formula

$$\int_0^\infty \frac{t^{\alpha-1}dt}{1+t} = \frac{\pi}{\sin\pi\alpha}. \qquad (0 < \alpha < 1) \qquad (1)$$

First we remark that, by Theorem 1, Chapter III, the integral $F(\alpha) = \int_0^\infty \frac{t^{\alpha-1}dt}{1+t}$ defines a continuous function of α in the range $(0,1)$. For if α is confined to the range $[a,b]$, where $a > 0$ and $b < 1$, we can easily construct a function $\phi(t)$ such that $\left| \frac{\partial}{\partial\alpha} \frac{t^{\alpha-1}}{1+t} \right| = \left| \frac{t^{\alpha-1}\log t}{1+t} \right| \leq \phi(t)$ and ϕ has a finite integral over the range $(0,\infty)$. Indeed, we need only put $\phi = \frac{-t^{a-1}\log t}{1+t}$ if $0 < t \leq 1$ and $\phi = \frac{t^{b-1}\log t}{1+t}$ if $t > 1$. It follows that if (r_n) is any sequence in the interval $(0,1)$ tending to α, then $F(r_n) \to F(\alpha)$. Since clearly $\frac{\pi}{\sin\pi r_n} \to \frac{\pi}{\sin\pi\alpha}$ the proof of (1) is accomplished if we can show that (1) holds for a particular sequence (r_n) of this kind. It will certainly be permissible to assume that r_n is rational, and we shall in fact prove (1) for any rational number r in $(0,1)$. This is equivalent to showing that

$$\int_0^\infty \frac{x^{2m-1}dx}{x^{2n}+1} = \frac{\pi}{2n\sin(m\pi/n)}$$

$$(m,n \text{ positive integers}, 0 < m < n) \qquad (2)$$

APPENDIX II

For, if in this formula we put $x = t^{1/2n}$, equation (2) becomes

$$\int_0^\infty \frac{t^{(m/n)-1}}{1+t} dt = \frac{\pi}{\sin (m\pi/n)},$$

which is identical with (1) for rational values of α. It is therefore sufficient to establish (2), which we shall proceed to do. It is convenient to rewrite the integral in the form

$$\int_0^\infty \frac{x^{2m-1}dx}{x^{2n}+1} = \int_0^1 \frac{x^{2m-1}dx}{x^{2n}+1} + \int_1^\infty \frac{x^{2m-1}dx}{x^{2n}+1}$$

$$= \int_0^1 \frac{x^{2m-1} + x^{2n-2m-1}}{1+x^{2n}} dx,$$

where in the second term of the middle member we have used $1/x$ instead of x as variable of integration. The rest of the work consists in carrying out the elementary, but somewhat laborious task of integrating the rational function $g(x) = \dfrac{x^{2m-1} + x^{2n-2m-1}}{1 + x^{2n}}$ by the method of partial fractions.

The roots of the equation $x^{2n} + 1 = 0$ are $a_k = e^{i\theta_k}$, where $\theta_k = \dfrac{\pi}{2n} (2k + 1)$ $(k = 0,1, ..., 2n - 1)$. The roots can be grouped into conjugate complex pairs a_k, a_k' where $k + k' = 2n - 1$. Setting up the partial fraction expansion $g(x) = \sum_{k=0}^{2n-1} C_k/(x - a_k)$, we find that

$$C_k = \lim_{x \to a_k} (x - a_k) \frac{x^{2m-1} + x^{2n-2m-1}}{x^{2n} + 1}$$

$$= \frac{a^{2m-1} + a_k^{2n-2m+1}}{2na_k^{2n-1}} = \frac{1}{2n}(-a_k^{2m} + a_k^{-2m}),$$

APPENDIX II

bearing in mind that

$$\lim_{x \to a_k} \frac{x^{2n} + 1}{x - a_k} = \lim_{x \to a_k} \frac{(x^{2n} + 1) - (a_k^{2n} + 1)}{x - a_k}$$

$$= \left[\frac{d}{dx} (x^{2n} + 1) \right]_{x = a_k} \text{ and } a_k^{2n} = -1.$$

Thus we have that $C_k = -\dfrac{i}{n} \sin 2m\theta_k$ and $C_{k'} = -C_k$

$= \dfrac{i}{n} \sin 2m\theta_k.$

Hence

$$g(x) = \sum_{k=0}^{n-1} \left(\frac{C_k}{x - a_k} + \frac{C_{k'}}{x - a_{k'}} \right)$$

$$= \frac{2}{n} \sum_{k=0}^{n-1} \frac{\sin 2m\theta_k \sin \theta_k}{x^2 - 2x \cos \theta_k + 1}.$$

Now for a fixed value of k,

$$\int_0^1 \frac{dx}{x^2 - 2x \cos \theta_k + 1} = \int_0^1 \frac{dx}{(x - \cos \theta_k)^2 + \sin^2 \theta_k}$$

$$= \frac{1}{\sin \theta_k} \left(\frac{\pi}{2} - \frac{\theta_k}{2} \right),$$

whence

$$\int_0^1 g(x)dx = \frac{2}{n} \sum_{k=0}^{n-1} \left(\frac{\pi}{2} - \frac{\theta_k}{2} \right) \sin 2m\theta_k$$

$$= \frac{2}{n} \sum_{k=0}^{n-1} \left(\frac{\pi}{2} - \frac{\pi(2k + 1)}{4n} \right) \sin \left\{ \frac{\pi m}{n} \left(2k + 1 \right) \right\}. \quad (3)$$

APPENDIX II

In order to evaluate this sum it is convenient to start from the identity

$$e^{i\omega} + e^{3i\omega} + \ldots + e^{(2n-1)i\omega} = e^{in\omega} \frac{\sin n\omega}{\sin \omega}.$$

Splitting the result into real and imaginary parts we find that

$$\sum_{0}^{n-1} \sin (2k + 1)\omega = \frac{\sin^2 n\omega}{\sin \omega},$$

$$\sum_{0}^{n-1} \cos (2k + 1)\omega = \tfrac{1}{2} \frac{\sin 2n\omega}{\sin \omega},$$

and on differentiating the second formula with respect to ω,

$$\sum_{0}^{n-1} (2k + 1) \sin (2k + 1)\omega$$

$$= \tfrac{1}{2} (2n \sin \omega \cos 2n\omega - \sin 2n\omega \cos \omega)(\sin \omega)^{-2}.$$

In order to apply these relations to (3) we have to put $\omega = \pi m/n$, in which case

$$\sum_{0}^{n-1} \sin (2k + 1)\omega = 0,$$

$$\sum_{0}^{n-1} (2k + 1) \sin (2k + 1)\omega = -n/\sin \omega,$$

$$\int_{0}^{1} g(x)dx = \frac{2}{n}\left(\frac{\pi}{4n} \frac{n}{\sin \omega}\right) = \frac{\pi}{2n} \frac{1}{\sin \omega},$$

which is (2).

Appendix III

We want to prove that

$$\lim_{n \to \infty} \int_0^n t^x \left(1 - \frac{t}{n}\right)^n dt = \int_0^\infty t^x e^{-t} dt \quad (x > -1). \tag{1}$$

Since the integral on the right converges, we know that

$$\int_0^\infty t^x e^{-t} dt = \lim_{n \to \infty} \int_0^n t^x e^{-t} dt.$$

It therefore suffices to prove that

$$\lim_{n \to \infty} \int_0^n t^x \left\{ e^{-t} - \left(1 - \frac{t}{n}\right)^n \right\} dt = 0. \tag{2}$$

We shall presently establish the inequality

$$0 \leqq 1 - e^t \left(1 - \frac{t}{n}\right)^n \leqq \frac{e}{2n} t^2 \quad (0 \leqq t \leqq n), \tag{3}$$

or, equivalently,

$$0 < e^{-t} - \left(1 - \frac{t}{n}\right)^n < \frac{e}{2n} t^2 e^{-t}.$$

Assuming this result for a moment it follows that

$$\int_0^n t^x \left\{ e^{-t} - \left(1 - \frac{t}{n}\right)^n \right\} dt \leqq \frac{e}{2n} \int_0^n t^{x+2} e^{-t} dt$$

$$< \frac{e}{2n} \int_0^\infty t^{x+2} e^{-t} dt = \frac{e}{2n} (x + 2)! \to 0,$$

as $n \to \infty$, which proves (2).

APPENDIX III

In order to establish (3) we start from the equations

$$1 - e^t \left(1 - \frac{t}{n}\right)^n = -\int_0^t \frac{d}{dv}\left\{e^v\left(1 - \frac{v}{n}\right)^n\right\}dv$$

$$= \int_0^t e^v\left(1 - \frac{v}{n}\right)^{n-1}\frac{v}{n}dv.$$

We can obtain an estimate for the last integral by examining the function

$$g(v) = e^v\left(1 - \frac{v}{n}\right)^{n-1}$$

in the range $(0,n)$. Since

$$g'(v) = e^v\left(1 - \frac{v}{n}\right)^{n-2}\frac{1}{n}(1 - v),$$

it follows that $g(v)$ attains its maximum when $v = 1$. Thus

$$g(v) \leqq g(1) = e\left(1 - \frac{1}{n}\right)^{n-1} \leqq e \qquad (0 \leqq v \leqq n).$$

Hence

$$\int_0^t e^v\left(1 - \frac{v}{n}\right)^{n-1}\frac{v}{n}dv$$

$$= \int_0^t g(v)\frac{v}{n}dv \leqq e\int_0^t \frac{v}{n}dv = \frac{e}{2n}t^2,$$

which is (3). This completes the proof of (1).

Appendix IV

When x is not a negative integer, equation (33) of Chapter IV is equivalent to

$$x! = e^{-\gamma x} \sum_{k=1}^{\infty} \left(1 + \frac{x}{k}\right)^{-1} e^{x/k}. \tag{1}$$

We want to prove that

$$\log x! = -\gamma x + \sum_{k=1}^{\infty} \left\{ \frac{x}{k} - \log\left(1 + \frac{x}{k}\right) \right\}, \tag{2}$$

that is we wish to justify taking the logarithm of the infinite product as if it consisted only of a finite number of factors.

In this context, x is a fixed real number. Therefore, if n is a sufficiently great integer

$$\left| \frac{x}{n} \right| \leqslant \tfrac{1}{2}. \tag{3}$$

When n is such an integer, it is convenient to write (1) in the form

$$x! = e^{-\gamma x} \prod_{k=1}^{n} \left(1 + \frac{x}{k}\right)^{-1} e^{x/k} P_n(x), \tag{4}$$

where

$$P_n(x) = \prod_{k=n+1}^{\infty} \left(1 + \frac{x}{k}\right)^{-1} e^{x/k}.$$

We shall now derive an estimate for $P_n(x)$. In the general term of the last product $\left| \frac{x}{k} \right| \leqq \tfrac{1}{2}$. Hence we may use the expansion

70

$$\left(1 + \frac{x}{k}\right)^{-1} e^{x/k} = \exp\left\{\frac{x}{k} - \log\left(1 + \frac{x}{k}\right)\right\}$$

$$= \exp\left\{\frac{x}{k} - \frac{x}{k} + \frac{1}{2}\left(\frac{x}{k}\right)^2 - \frac{1}{3}\left(\frac{x}{k}\right)^3 + \ldots\right\}$$

$$\leqq \exp\left\{\frac{1}{2}\left(\frac{x}{k}\right)^2\left(1 + \frac{2}{3}\left|\frac{x}{k}\right| + \frac{2}{4}\left|\frac{x}{k}\right|^2 + \ldots\right)\right\}$$

$$\leqq \exp\left\{\frac{1}{2}\left(\frac{x}{k}\right)^2\left(1 + \left|\frac{x}{k}\right| + \left|\frac{x}{k}\right|^2 + \ldots\right)\right\}$$

$$\leqq \exp\left\{\frac{1}{2}\left(\frac{x}{k}\right)^2\left(1 + \frac{1}{2} + \frac{1}{4} + \ldots\right)\right\} = \exp\left(\frac{x}{k}\right)^2.$$

It follows that

$$P_n(x) \leqq \exp\left\{x^2\left(\frac{1}{(n+1)^2} + \frac{1}{(n+2)^2} + \ldots\right)\right\}. \qquad (5)$$

Since (4) involves only a finite product, when P_n is counted as a single factor, we may deduce that

$$\log x! = -\gamma x + \sum_{k=1}^{n}\left\{\frac{x}{k} - \log\left(1 + \frac{x}{k}\right)\right\} + \log P_n(x),$$

or, alternatively

$$\log x! + \gamma x - \sum_{k=1}^{n}\left\{\frac{x}{k} - \log\left(1 + \frac{x}{k}\right)\right\} = \log P_n(x). \qquad (6)$$

By (5) $\log P_n(x) \leqq x^2 \sum_{k=n+1}^{\infty} k^{-2}$. Since Σk^{-2} is a convergent series, it follows* that $\lim_{n\to\infty} \sum_{k=n+1}^{\infty} k^{-2} = 0$. Hence we obtain (2) by letting n tend to infinity in (6).

In order to establish the equations (34) and (35) of Chapter IV, we use the temporary notations

* See J. A. Green, *loc. cit.* Example 4, p. 32.

$$L_1(x) = -\gamma + \sum_{k=1}^{\infty} \left(\frac{1}{k} - \frac{1}{x+k}\right),$$

$$L_2(x) = \sum_{k=1}^{\infty} \frac{1}{(x+k)^2}. \tag{7}$$

As before, let n be a positive integer satisfying (3). Consider the integral

$$\int_0^x L_2(u)du = \int_0^x \left(\sum_{k=1}^n \frac{1}{(u+k)^2}\right)du + \int_0^x \left(\sum_{k=n+1}^{\infty} \frac{1}{(u+k)^2}\right)du.$$

Since a finite series can be integrated term by term,

$$\int_0^x \sum_{k=1}^n \frac{1}{(u+k)^2}du = \sum_{k=1}^n \int_0^x \frac{du}{(u+k)^2} = \sum_{k=1}^n \left(\frac{1}{k} - \frac{1}{x+k}\right).$$

Next, when $k < n$, we have that $\left|\frac{u}{k}\right| \leq \frac{1}{2}$ and hence $(u+k)^{-2}$ $= k^{-2}\left(1 + \frac{u}{k}\right)^{-2} \leq 4k^{-2}$. It follows that

$$\left|\int_0^x \left(\sum_{k=n+1}^{\infty} \frac{1}{(u+k)^2}\right)du\right| \leq 4 \int_0^x \left(\sum_{k=n+1}^{\infty} k^{-2}\right)du$$

$$= 4|x| \sum_{k=n+1}^{\infty} k^{-2}.$$

As before, the truncated infinite series on the right tends to zero as n tends to infinity, and we can infer that

$$\int_0^x L_2(u)du = \sum_{k=1}^{\infty} \left(\frac{1}{k} - \frac{1}{x+k}\right) = \gamma + L_1(x). \tag{8}$$

APPENDIX IV

On differentiating with respect to x we obtain that
$$L_2(x) = L_1'(x).$$
By an analogous argument we shall show that
$$L_1(x) = \frac{d}{dx} \log x!. \tag{9}$$
In fact,

$$\int_0^x L_1(u)du = \int_0^x \left\{ -\gamma + \sum_{k=1}^n \left(\frac{1}{k} - \frac{1}{u+k} \right) \right.$$
$$\left. + \sum_{k=n+1}^\infty \left(\frac{1}{k} + \frac{1}{u+k} \right) \right\} du$$

$$= -\gamma x + \sum_{k=1}^n \left(\frac{x}{k} - \log\left(1+\frac{x}{k}\right) \right) + \int_0^x \left\{ \sum_{k=n+1}^\infty \left(\frac{1}{k} - \frac{1}{u+k} \right) \right\} du$$

Now $\left| \dfrac{1}{k} - \dfrac{1}{u+k} \right| = \left| \dfrac{u}{k(u+k)} \right| = \dfrac{1}{k^2} \left| \dfrac{u}{(1+u/k)} \right| \leqq \dfrac{2|u|}{k^2}$,

since $u/k \geqq -\frac{1}{2}$ by our choice of n. It follows that

$$\left| \int_0^x \left\{ \sum_{k=n+1}^\infty \left(\frac{1}{k} - \frac{1}{u+k} \right) \right\} du \right|$$

$$\leqq 2 \sum_{k=n+1}^\infty k^{-2} \left| \int_0^x |u|d|u| \right| = x^2 \sum_{k=n+1}^\infty k^{-2}.$$

On letting n tend to infinity we deduce that
$$\int_0^x L_1(u)du = \log x!.$$
On differentiating with respect to x we establish (9). It is clear that (8) and (9) together are equivalent to the results required.

Solutions for Exercises

Chapter I

1. (i) $\displaystyle\sum_{k=1}^{n} \left(\frac{k}{n}\right)^s \frac{1}{n} \to \int_0^1 x^s dx$; (ii) $\displaystyle\sum_{k=1}^{n} \frac{1}{n+k} = \sum_{k=1}^{n} \frac{1}{1+(k/n)} \frac{1}{n} \to \int_0^1 \frac{dx}{1+x}$;

(iii) $\displaystyle\sum_{k=1}^{n} n^{-\frac{1}{2}}(ka+n)^{-\frac{1}{2}} = \sum_{k=1}^{n} (1/n)\{a(k/n)+1\}^{-\frac{1}{2}} \to \int_0^1 (ax+1)^{-\frac{1}{2}}dx$.

2. (i) Integrate by parts twice; (ii) put $y = \tan x$, $T_n =$

$$\int y^{n-2}(y'-1)\,dx = \int y^{n-2}y'dx - \int y^{n-2}dx = (1/n-1)y^{n-1} - T_{n-2};$$

(iii) put $y = (2ax - x^2)^{\frac{1}{2}}$, $yy' = a - x$, $J_n =$

$$\int_0^{2a} x^{n-1}\{a -(a-x)\}ydx = aJ_{n-1} - \int_0^{2a} x^{n-1}y^2y'dx =$$

$$aJ_{n-1} - \tfrac{1}{3}\int_0^{2a} x^{n-1}(y^3)'dx = aJ_{n-1} + \frac{n-1}{3}\int_0^{2a} x^{n-2}(2ax-x^2)ydx =$$

$aJ_{n-1} + \dfrac{n-1}{3}2aJ_{n-1} - \dfrac{n-1}{3}J_n$; (iv) $P_{m,n} = -\dfrac{1}{n} \cos^m x \cos nx - $
$(m/n)\int \cos^{m-1} x \sin x \cos nx\,dx$, note that $\sin x \cos nx = \sin (n-1)x$ and prove the second part by induction; (v) integration by parts, for second part see footnote on p. 35.

SOLUTIONS FOR EXERCISES

3. (i) (put $u = e^{x/2}$), $(e^{2x} + e^x)^{\frac{1}{2}} + \log\{(e^x + 1)^{\frac{1}{2}} + e^{x/2}\}$; (ii)

$\sin^{-1}\left(\dfrac{2x + 3}{\sqrt{13}}\right)$; (iii) $\left(\text{put } y = \dfrac{1}{x}\right)$, $\dfrac{1}{\sqrt{6}}\cos^{-1}\left(\dfrac{12 - x}{5x}\right)$; (iv)

$\frac{1}{3}\log\{x(3 - x^2)^4\}$; (v) $\dfrac{1}{10}\log\{(x-5)^3(x+15)^7\}$; (vi) (put $\sin^{-1}x = \theta$),
$\exp(a\sin^{-1}x)\{a(1 - x^2)^{\frac{1}{2}} + x\}(a^2 + 1)^{-1}$.

4. Put $\tan\theta = t^2$, note that $t^4 + 1 = (t^2 - t\sqrt{2} + 1)(t^2 + t\sqrt{2} + 1)$ and $(\sqrt{2} - 1)(\sqrt{2} + 1) = 1$.

5. The substitution $x = y^{-1}$ is inadmissible in a range that includes $x = 0$.

Chapter II

1. (i) integrand behaves like $x^{-\frac{1}{2}}$ at $x = 0$: conv.

   (ii) integrand behaves like $x^{-\frac{1}{2}}$ at $x = 0$: conv.

   (iii) integrand behaves like x^{-2} at ∞: conv.

   (iv) integrand behaves like $(x - 1)^{-1}$ at $x = 1$: div.

   (v) integrand behaves like e^{-x^2} at ∞: conv.

   (vi) integrand behaves like $(\pi/2 - x)^{-\frac{1}{2}}$ at $x = \pi/2$: conv.

2. In the interval $[0,1]$ the integrand behaves like x^{p-1}: conv; in the interval $[1,\infty]$ the integrand behaves like x^{-2+p}: conv. Hence integral over $[0,\infty]$ converges; $\displaystyle\int_0^\infty \frac{x^{\alpha-1}}{1 + x^\beta}dx = \frac{1}{\beta}\int_0^\infty \frac{t^{\alpha/\beta-1}}{1 + t}dt \ (x^\beta = t)$.

3. At $x = 0$, $(\sin x)^{-\lambda}$ behaves like $x^{-\lambda}$; at $x = \pi$, $(\sin x)^{-\lambda}$ behaves like $(\pi - x)^{-\lambda}$; in each case the integral converges.

SOLUTIONS FOR EXERCISES

4. At $s = 0$, the integrand can be expanded as $s^{-2}e^{-s}(e^s - 1 - s) =$
$s^{-2}e^{-s}\left(\dfrac{1}{3!}s^3 + \dfrac{1}{4!}s^4 \dots\right)$ and is therefore regular; for sufficiently
great s, $(1 + s)e^{-s} < 1$, and the integrand is less than s^{-2}, which
ensures the convergence of the integral.

5. See solution to ex. 4 of Chapter I.

6 and 7. Write $\displaystyle\int_0^\infty = \int_0^1 + \int_1^\infty$ and make the substitution $x = y^{-1}$
in the second integral.

8. Let $x = e^t$. Then $\dfrac{x}{(\log x)^\alpha} = \dfrac{e^t}{t^\alpha}$, which tends to infinity as t tends
to infinity.

Hence $x > (\log x)^\alpha$ for sufficiently great x, and $\displaystyle\int_0^\infty (\log x)^{-\alpha}dx >$
$\displaystyle\int_2^\infty x^{-1}dx$, which diverges.

9. Make the substitution $x = e^t$ and use example 4 of p. 22.

10. $\frac{1}{4} < k < 1$.

11. Put $t = \tan\frac{1}{2}\theta$, then $d\theta = \dfrac{2dt}{1 + t^2}$, $\cos\theta = \dfrac{1 - t^2}{1 + t^2}$ and
$$\int_0^\pi \frac{d\theta}{1 + a\cos\theta} = \int_0^\infty \frac{2dt}{(1 + a) + (1 - a)t^2} =$$
$$\frac{2}{\sqrt{(1 - a^2)}}\left[\tan^{-1}\left(\frac{1 - a}{1 + a}\right)t\right]_0^\infty = \pi(1 - a^2)^{-\frac{1}{2}}.$$

Chapter III

2. Use formula (5) of p. 32.

76

SOLUTIONS FOR EXERCISES

3. (i) Evaluate both sides of the equation $\int_0^\infty dx \int_a^b e^{-tx} dt =$

$\int_b^a dt \int_0^\infty e^{-tx} dx$. (ii) Let $I(r) = \int_0^\infty \frac{1}{x}(e^{-ax} - e^{-bx}) \cos rx\, dx$. Then $I'(r) =$

$\int_0^\infty (e^{-bx} - e^{-ax}) \sin rx\, dx = \dfrac{r}{b^2 + r^2} - \dfrac{r}{a^2 + r^2}$ by equation (I, 22).

It follows that $I(r) = \frac{1}{2} \log\left(\dfrac{b^2 + r^2}{a^2 + r^2}\right) + c$, and $c = 0$ by 3(i).

4. The integral is equal to $\displaystyle\int_0^\pi d\theta \int_{-a}^a \frac{dt}{1 + t \cos\theta} = \int_{-a}^a dt \int_0^\pi \frac{d\theta}{1 + t \cos\theta}$

$= \pi \displaystyle\int_{-a}^a (1 - t^2)^{-\frac{1}{2}} dt$ (ex. 11, p. 26) $= 2\pi \sin^{-1} a$.

5. The result is trivial when $p = 0$. Assume that $0 < p < 1$. Put
$t = 2\theta$ in equation (III, 11), then $0 = \displaystyle\int_0^{\pi/2} \log\{(1 - x)^2 + 4x \sin^2 \theta\}\, d\theta$,

if $|x| < 1$. Choose x such that $|x| < 1$ and $4x =$

$-p(1 - x)^2$, thus $x = \{p - 2 + 2\sqrt{(1 - p)}\}/p$; hence
$\displaystyle\int_0^{\pi/2} \log(1 - p \sin^2 \theta) d\theta = -\pi \log(1 - x) = \pi \log\frac{1}{2}\{1 + \sqrt{(1 - p)}\}$.

For the second part put $p = 1$.

6. In equation (III, 12) put $t = \alpha x$ and note that the limits of integration become $(0, \infty)$ or $(0, -\infty)$, according as $\alpha > 0$ or $\alpha < 0$.

7. $\displaystyle\int_0^\infty \frac{\sin^2 x}{x^2}dx = \left[-\frac{\sin^2 x}{x}\right]_0^\infty + \int_0^\infty \frac{2\sin x \cos x}{x}dx$

$\displaystyle = 0 + \int_0^\infty \frac{\sin 2x}{x}dx = \frac{\pi}{2}$ by the preceding exercise.

8. Put $x = a\tan\theta$. The integral becomes $-2a\displaystyle\int_0^{\pi/2}(\log\sin\theta)\sec^2\theta\, d\theta$

$= -2a[(\log\sin\theta)\tan\theta]_0^{\pi/2} + 2a\displaystyle\int_0^{\pi/2} d\theta = \pi a$, the integrated function being zero at both end points, since $\lim_{\theta\to 0}\tan\theta\,(\log\sin\theta) =$

$\lim_{x\to 0} x\log x = 0$ and $\lim_{\theta\to\pi/2}\tan\theta\,(\log\sin\theta) = \lim_{t\to 0}\dfrac{\log\cos t}{\tan t} = 0$ (e.g. by

de l'Hospital's Rule, see P. J. Hilton, *loc. cit.* p. 40, Theorem 3.9.).

Chapter IV

1. In formula (IV, 18) write $\displaystyle\int_0^\infty \ldots dv = \int_0^1 \ldots dv + \int_1^\infty \ldots dv$, put $v = t$ in the first integral and $v = t^{-1}$ in the second integral and express the sum as a single integral.

2. (i) Put $x = t^{-1}$, the integral becomes $\displaystyle\int_0^1 t^{3/2}(1-t)^{3/2}dt =$

$\left(\dfrac{3}{2}\right)!\left(\dfrac{3}{2}\right)!/4! = \dfrac{3\pi}{128}$; (ii) put $4x = t$, the integral becomes

$2^9\displaystyle\int_0^1 t^2\,(1-t)^{3/2}dt = 2^9\,2!\left(\dfrac{3}{2}\right)!/\left(\dfrac{9}{2}\right)!$.

SOLUTIONS FOR EXERCISES

3. (i) Put $x(ax + b)^{-1} = (a + b)^{-1}t$; (ii) put $1 + x = t$; (iii) put $\sin^2 \theta = t$ and use part (i).

4. Put $t = (x - a)/(b - a)$; the integral becomes

$$(b - a)\int_0^1 t^{-\alpha+1}(1 - t)^{\alpha-1}dt + a \int_0^1 t^{-\alpha}(1 - t)^{\alpha-1}dt$$

$$= \frac{\pi}{\sin \pi\alpha}\{\alpha a + (1 - \alpha)b\} \text{ by (IV, 28).}$$

5. Put $x = t^{\frac{1}{2}}$ and use (IV, 28).

6. (i) Put $t = ns$ in (IV, 30) and use (IV, 21); (ii) is equivalent to (i) after Γ and B have been expressed in terms of the factorial function.

7. Equivalently, show that $\int_{-\infty}^{\infty} \frac{\cosh \alpha x}{\cosh x}dx = \frac{\pi}{\cos (\frac{1}{2}\alpha\pi)}$.

Put $t = e^{2x}$. The integral becomes $\frac{1}{2} \int_0^{\infty} \frac{t^{(\alpha-1)/2} + t^{-\alpha(+1)/2}}{1 + t}dt$, which can be evaluated by two applications of (IV, 27).

8. By (IV, 45), $(\pi n)^{\frac{1}{2}}2^{-2n}\frac{(2n)!}{(n!)^2} = \frac{\rho(2n)}{\{\rho(n)\}^2} \to 1$. Observe that

$$\frac{2.2.4.4 \ldots 2n.2n}{1.3.3.5 \ldots 2n - 1.2n + 1} = \frac{2^{4n}(n!)^4}{\{(2n)!\}^2\pi n} \cdot \frac{\pi n}{2n + 1}, \text{ which tends to}$$

$\pi/2$ by the preceding result.

List of Formulae

I. *Indefinite Integrals*
(Constants of integration are omitted)

1. $\int x^a dx = \dfrac{1}{a+1} x^{a+1} \quad (a \neq -1)$

2. $\int \dfrac{dx}{x} = \log |x|$

3. $\int e^x dx = e^x$

4. $\int \sin x\, dx = -\cos x$

5. $\int \cos x\, dx = \sin x$

6. $\int \tan x\, dx = -\log |\cos x|$

7. $\int \cot x\, dx = \log |\sin x|$

8. $\int \dfrac{dx}{\cos x} = \log \left| \tan \left(\dfrac{\pi}{4} + \dfrac{x}{2} \right) \right|$

9. $\int \dfrac{dx}{\sin x} = \log \left| \tan \tfrac{1}{2} x \right|$

10. $\int \dfrac{dx}{\cos^2 x} = \tan x$

LIST OF FORMULAE

11. $\int \dfrac{dx}{\sin^2 x} = -\cot x$

12. $\int \sin^2 x \, dx = \frac{1}{2}(x - \sin x \cos x)$

13. $\int \cos^2 x \, dx = \frac{1}{2}(x + \sin x \cos x)$

14. $\int \dfrac{dx}{x^2 + a^2} = \dfrac{1}{a} \tan^{-1} \left(\dfrac{x}{a} \right)$

15. $\int \dfrac{dx}{x^2 - a^2} = \dfrac{1}{2a} \log \dfrac{x - a}{x + a}$, if $|x| > a > 0$.

16. $\int (a^2 - x^2)^{-\frac{1}{2}} dx = \sin^{-1}(x/a) \quad (a > 0)$

17.* $\int (x^2 + a^2)^{-\frac{1}{2}} dx = \sinh^{-1}(x/a)$ or $\log \{(x^2 + a^2)^{\frac{1}{2}} + x\}$

18.* $\int (x^2 - a^2)^{-\frac{1}{2}} dx = \cosh^{-1}(x/a)$ or $\log \{x + (x^2 - a^2)^{\frac{1}{2}}\}$

19. $\int (a^2 - x^2)^{\frac{1}{2}} dx = -\frac{1}{2}a^2 \cos^{-1}(x/a) + \frac{1}{2}x(a^2 - x^2)^{\frac{1}{2}}$

20. $\int (x^2 - a^2)^{\frac{1}{2}} dx = -\frac{1}{2}a^2 \cosh^{-1}(x/a) + \frac{1}{2}x(x^2 - a^2)^{\frac{1}{2}}$

21. $\int (x^2 + a^2)^{\frac{1}{2}} dx = \frac{1}{2}a^2 \sinh^{-1}(x/a) + \frac{1}{2}x(x^2 + a^2)^{\frac{1}{2}}$

22. $\int e^{ax} \cos bx \, dx = \dfrac{e^{ax}}{a^2 + b^2} (a \cos bx + b \sin bx)$

* $\sinh^{-1} x$ is the unique real number u satisfying $e^u = x + (x^2 + 1)^{\frac{1}{2}}$; $\cosh^{-1} x$ $(x \geqq 1)$ is the unique non-negative number v satisfying $e^v = x + (x^2 - 1)^{\frac{1}{2}}$.

81

LIST OF FORMULAE

23. $\displaystyle \int e^{ax} \sin bx\, dx = \frac{e^{ax}}{a^2 + b^2}(a \sin bx - b \cos bx)$

II. *Recurrence Formulae*

24. $\displaystyle \int \sin^m x \cos^n x\, dx = \frac{\sin^{m+1}x \cos^{n-1}x}{m + n} + \frac{n - 1}{m + n}\int \sin^m x \cos^{n-2}x\, dx$

$\displaystyle \qquad = -\frac{\sin^{m-1}x \cos^{n+1}x}{m + n} + \frac{n - 1}{m + n}\int \sin^{m-2}x \cos^n x\, dx$

(p. 13)

25. $\displaystyle \int \frac{dx}{(x^2 + 1)^n} = \frac{x}{2(n-1)(x^2+1)^{n-1}} + \frac{2n-3}{2(n-1)}\int \frac{dx}{(x^2+1)^{n-1}} \quad (n \neq 1).$

26. $\displaystyle \int x^a (\log x)^n dx = \frac{x^{a+1}(\log x)^n}{a + 1} - \frac{a}{a + 1}\int x^a (\log x)^{n-1} dx \quad (a \neq -1).$

III. *Definite Integrals*

27. $\displaystyle \int_{-\pi}^{\pi} \sin mx \sin nx\, dx = \begin{cases} 0 \text{ if } m \neq n \\ \pi \text{ if } m = n, n \neq 0 \end{cases}$

28. $\displaystyle \int_{-\pi}^{\pi} \cos mx \cos nx\, dx = \begin{cases} 0 \text{ if } m \neq n \\ \pi \text{ if } m = n, n \neq 0 \end{cases}$

29. $\displaystyle \int_{-\pi}^{\pi} \sin mx \cos nx\, dx = 0$

30. $\displaystyle \int_{0}^{\pi} \frac{d\theta}{a + b \cos\theta} = \pi(a^2 - b^2)^{-\frac{1}{2}} \quad (|a| > |b|).$

31. $\displaystyle \int_{0}^{\infty} \frac{\sin x}{x} dx = \tfrac{1}{2}\pi \quad$ (p. 38)

32. $\displaystyle \int_{0}^{\infty} e^{-x^2} dx = \tfrac{1}{2}\sqrt{\pi} \quad$ (p. 50)

LIST OF FORMULAE

33. $\displaystyle\int_0^{\pi/2} \sin^n x\, dx = \int_0^{\pi/2} \cos^n x\, dx = \begin{cases} \dfrac{(n-1)(n-3)\dots 3}{n(n-2)\dots 2}\dfrac{\pi}{2} & (n\text{ even}) \\[2mm] \dfrac{(n-1)(n-3)\dots 2}{n(n-2)\dots 3} & (n\text{ odd}), \end{cases}$ (p. 14)

34. $\displaystyle\int_0^{\infty} \log(1 - 2x\cos t + x^2)dt = \begin{cases} 0, \text{ if } |x| \leqq 1 \\ \pi \log x^2, \text{ if } |x| \leqq 1 \end{cases}$ (p. 37)

IV. *The Factorial Function*

35. $\displaystyle x! = \int_0^{\infty} t^x e^{-t} dt \quad (x > -1)$ (p. 43)

35a. $\displaystyle \Gamma(x) = (x-1)! = \int_0^{\infty} t^{x-1} e^{-t} dt \quad (x > 0)$

36. $(x+1)! = (x+1)x! \quad (x > -1)$

(p. 43)

36a. $\Gamma(x+1) = (x+1)\Gamma(x) \quad (x > 0)$

37. $(-\tfrac{1}{2})! = \sqrt{\pi} = 2(\tfrac{1}{2})!$ (p. 50)

38. $\displaystyle B(x,y) = \int_0^1 t^{x-1}(1-t)^{y-1} dt \quad (x > 0, y > 0)$ (p. 45)

39. $\displaystyle \int_0^1 t^x (1-t)^y dt = \frac{x!\, y!}{(x+y+1)!} \quad (x > -1, y > -1)$ (p. 21)

40. $\displaystyle \int_0^{\pi/2} \sin^m\theta \cos^n\theta\, d\theta = \frac{1}{2}\frac{\{\tfrac{1}{2}(m-1)\}!\,\{\tfrac{1}{2}(n-1)\}!}{\{\tfrac{1}{2}(m+n)\}!}$ (p. 50)

41. $(2x)! = \pi^{-\frac{1}{2}} 2^{2x} x!\,(x - \tfrac{1}{2})!$ (p. 51)

42. $\displaystyle \int_0^{\infty} \frac{v^{x-1} dv}{1+v} = \frac{\pi}{\sin \pi x} \quad (0 < x < 1)$ (p. 51)

43. $x!\,(-x)! = \pi x/\sin \pi x \quad (0 < x < 1)$ (p. 52)

LIST OF FORMULAE

44. $x! = \lim_{n \to \infty} \dfrac{n^x n!}{(x+1)(x+2) \dots (x+n)}$ ($x \neq$ neg. integer) (p. 53)

45. $\sin \pi x = \pi x \displaystyle\prod_{k=1}^{\infty} \left(1 - \dfrac{x^2}{k^2}\right)$ (p. 53)

46. $\dfrac{1}{x!} = e^{\gamma x} \displaystyle\prod_{k=1}^{\infty} \left(1 + \dfrac{x}{k}\right) e^{-x/k}$ (p. 54)

47. $\log x! = -\gamma x + \displaystyle\sum_{k=1}^{\infty} \left\{\dfrac{x}{k} - \log\left(1 + \dfrac{x}{k}\right)\right\}$ (p. 54)

48. $\dfrac{d}{dx} \log x! = -\gamma + \displaystyle\sum_{k=1}^{\infty} \left(\dfrac{1}{k} - \dfrac{1}{(x+k)}\right)$ (p. 55)

49. $\dfrac{d^2}{dx^2} \log x! = \displaystyle\sum_{k=1}^{\infty} \dfrac{1}{(x+k)^2}$ (p. 55)

50. $\alpha! \sim (2\pi\alpha)^{\frac{1}{2}} (\alpha/e)^{\alpha}$ (Stirling's formula) (p. 59)

Index

Asymptotic formula for $x!$, 49

Beta function, 45

Conditionally convergent integral, 23

Differentiation under integral sign, 28
Divergent integral, 19
Dummy variable, 6
Duplication formula for $x!$, 51

Euler's constant, 54
Euler's First Integral, 45
Euler's Second Integral, 42
Existence Theorem, 4
Extension formula for $x!$, 52

Factorial function, 43
Fundamental theorem, 8

Gamma function, 43

Improper integrals, 18
Indefinite integrals, 9
Integral (definition), 3
Integration under integral sign, 33

Mean Value Theorem (First), 7

Norm of subdivision, 3

Primitive, 1
Product formula for $\sin \pi x$, 53
Product formula for $x!$, 53

Reduction formulae, 13
Riemann-Lebesgue Lemma, 62

Stirling's formula, 59
Subdivision, 2

Wallis's Product, 61